ROLLS-ROYCE HERI

THE ROLLS-ROYCE CRECY

Nahum, Foster-Pegg and Birch

HISTORICAL SERIES No 21

Published in 1994 by the
Rolls-Royce Heritage Trust
P O Box 31 Derby England

ISBN: 1 872922 05 8

The Historical Series is published as a joint initiative by the Rolls-Royce Heritage Trust and The Sir Henry Royce Memorial Foundation.

Also published in the series:

No.1 Rolls-Royce – the formative years 1906-1939
Alec Harvey-Bailey, published by RRHT

No.2 The Merlin in perspective – the combat years
Alec Harvey-Bailey, published by RRHT

No.3 Rolls-Royce – the pursuit of excellence
Alec Harvey-Bailey and Mike Evans, published by HRMF

No.4 In the beginning – the Manchester origins of
Rolls-Royce, Mike Evans, published by RRHT

No.5 Rolls-Royce – the Derby Bentleys
Alec Harvey-Bailey, published by HRMF

No.6 The early days of Rolls-Royce – and the Montagu family
Lord Montagu of Beaulieu, published by RRHT

No.7 Rolls-Royce – Hives, the quiet tiger
Alec Harvey-Bailey, published by HRMF

No.8 Rolls-Royce – Twenty to Wraith
Alec Harvey-Bailey, published by HRMF

No.9 Rolls-Royce and the Mustang
David Birch, published by RRHT

No.10 From Gipsy to Gem with diversions, 1926-1986
Peter Stokes, published by RRHT

No.11 Armstrong Siddeley – the Parkside story, 1896-1939
Ray Cook, published by RRHT

No.12 Henry Royce – mechanic
Donald Bastow, published by RRHT

No.14 Rolls-Royce – the sons of Martha
Alec Harvey-Bailey, published by HRMF

No.15 Olympus – the first forty years
Alan Baxter, published by RRHT

No.16 Rolls-Royce piston aero engines – a designer remembers
A A Rubbra, published by RRHT

No.17 Charlie Rolls – pioneer aviator
Gordon Bruce, published by RRHT

No.18 The Rolls-Royce Dart – pioneering turboprop
Roy Heathcote, published by RRHT

No.19 The Merlin 100 series – the ultimate military development
Alec Harvey-Bailey and Dave Piggott, published by RRHT

No.20 Rolls-Royce – Hives' turbulent barons
Alec Harvey-Bailey, published by HRMF

Technical series:

No.1 Rolls-Royce and the Rateau patents
Harry Pearson, published by RRHT

No.2 The vital spark! The development of aero-engine sparking plugs.
Keith Gough, published by RRHT

Books are available from:
The Library, Rolls-Royce plc, Moor Lane, PO Box 31, Derby DE24 8BJ

The Club Shop, Rolls-Royce Enthusiasts Club, The Hunt House, High Street, Paulespury
Northamptonshire NN12 7NA

Typesetting and Reproduction by Image Creation, Arnold, Nottingham
Printed by Premier Print, Ilkeston Road, Nottingham

CONTENTS

FOREWORD

Unusually, for a title from the Rolls-Royce Heritage Trust, this book presents the history of an engine from three different viewpoints. The story is set on its way by Andrew Nahum, the Curator of the Aeronautical Collection at the Science Museum. His story was first presented in a lecture to the Trust in October 1988 and he has based his account on the policy-making process at the Air Ministry which sought to bring forward the best possible engines for British air defence, and work done by Harry Ricardo and his engine consultancy at Shoreham where the complex concept of a sleeve-valve, stratified-charge, petrol-injection, two-stroke originated. The lecture was attended by a few of those still around who were directly concerned with the engine. Among them was Spike Corbitt, who never lost his enthusiasm for the Crecy.

One absentee from the lecture who had fought in the 'battle of Crecy' was Dick Foster-Pegg, long resident in the USA and who is now an independent consultant on gas turbine and steam powerplants. Dick describes the engine in detail and has put together his reminiscences of his time as a Crecy tester.

Finally, I have tried to put the Crecy into perspective, and have described what the concept might have led to. It might be thought that there is not a lot that could be said about an engine of which only six were built, none of which flew in an aircraft, and never ventured away from the Derby testbeds during its running life of less than two thousand hours. In fact, this study has revealed how much attention was given to this exotic engine concept and, in an effort to give the reader a glimpse of what might have been, I have collected together in a final chapter what the visionaries had in store for it and its developments.

I have also scoured the Company archives and retrieved all existing reports on Derby petrol-injection, two-stroke developments. From these I have expanded on what Andrew and Dick have written and also filled in some of the gaps. The reports proved particularly useful in providing illustrations of some of the mechanical features referred to in the text. Most, if not all, were in blueprint form and these have had to be 'reversed' to black line on white and redrawn. Here and there a little of the clarity may have been lost.

There are clearly differences in emphasis and approach in these accounts and by presenting them as individually-authored chapters, rather than trying to massage them into one edited account, there is the risk of overlap and even of contradictions. We accept this risk, for there is no such thing as exact history, and with the Crecy in particular, conceptions, even at the time, did not always agree. What is certain is that the Crecy was an unusually complex and fascinating project and that this book represents the most complete attempt that there has been to tell its tale.

I am grateful for help received from ex-Crecy men Ken Fozard, Ken Herbert, Ray Hart and to Geoff Wilde for allowing his thoughts and opinions on the Crecy to add technical insight into the engine's unique characteristics.

David Birch

INTRODUCTION

The Crecy was perhaps the most revolutionary piston aero-engine ever to be developed by a major manufacturer. It incorporated several radical features and promised both a specific power output and a power density that could not be obtained by more usual designs. However, it was ultimately a revolution that failed, for the gas turbine, not the two-stroke, proved to be the successor to the highly-developed conventional piston engines like the Merlin.

At a time when few people in Britain even knew about the existence of radar the Crecy was conceived as a 'sprint' engine to enable fighters to take-off and climb to height in the short period of warning that radar would give. Paradoxically, at the end of its life, it held out the promise of superb fuel consumption for long-range operation. Another paradox is that it employed a number of exotic engineering solutions which had seldom been tried before and never combined together in an aero-engine and yet it also embodied elements which its initiator, Harry Ricardo, had borne with him since he first developed a passion for internal combustion engines as a schoolboy at the turn of the century.

Events made the Crecy obsolete before its development was complete. However, it remains a virtuoso achievement in the annals of internal-combustion engineering. At Rolls-Royce, at Ricardos and at the Royal Aircraft Establishment, Farnborough, engineers and scientists contributed impressive abilities to the project. Creativity and originality, intellectual analysis, sheer persistence in mechanical development – these are not diminished by the historical events which led to the aeronautical two-stroke being overtaken by the gas turbine. Let this book be a record of effort and a tribute to such admirable human qualities.

A.N.

THE ROLLS-ROYCE CRECY

CHAPTER ONE

Harry Ricardo – early mechanical influences

by Andrew Nahum

It may seem odd that an account of a Rolls-Royce project during the Second World War should start with the experiences of an engineer while still at school in the closing years of the nineteenth century, but that is how far back we must go to trace the true origins of the Crecy. This account may even seem too antiquarian to some, but it is unusual to be able to uncover so well the combined influences which eventually lead to the design of a new type of machine. In this case though, these influences can be unearthed to a remarkably complete degree and are of great interest to students of engine history.

Harry Ricardo is well known for his contribution to internal combustion engineering, particularly for the design of the 'Comet' cylinder head which first made feasible the small high-speed diesel for automotive use and also for his 'squish-type' head which extended the production life of the side-valve piston engine between the wars. However, his influence on the direction taken by the British piston aero-engine is probably still not appreciated. For example, it appears to have been his sole advocacy to the Aeronautical Research Committee, and to a sceptical Roy Fedden, that led to the Bristol company adopting the sleeve valve – a difficult and expensive solution – for its engines. This also led to its eventual adoption by Napiers for their Sabre and Rolls-Royce for the Exe, Eagle 22 and Pennine.

Harry Ricardo aboard a motor launch on the Thames c.1910. The engine appears to be a pre-1898 De Dion or De Dion-type, possibly adapted by Ricardo himself for the boat because it was obsolete and cheap.

The Crecy, too, used a single-sleeve valve of a particular type developed by Ricardo, but there were many other elements in the design which were echoes of the earliest features that had impressed him as a young boy with a passion for engines.

By the time that Ricardo went to Rugby school in 1898 he had owned a screw-cutting lathe since the age of ten, had built three steam engines, two to his own design, and, by his own account, was "fairly well-versed in the theory of both the steam and the internal combustion engine". He was also undertaking the design and manufacture of a petrol engine to raise water from a well at the family house in Sussex.

Even at this early date students of internal combustion were aware of the inefficiency imposed by the restriction of airflow when an engine is controlled by throttling the mixture. The problem is that if, instead, a spark-ignition engine is regulated by limiting the fuel supply, rather than fuel and air together, the mixture may become too lean for ignition to occur. (This difficulty does not, of course, arise in a diesel where injected fuel ignites spontaneously in an excess of air already heated by compression). A solution to the problem in spark-ignition engines is to produce an unequal distribution or 'stratification' of the fuel in the cylinder so that a rich-enough mixture will still be found close to the sparking plug. Ricardo recalled "During the previous Christmas holidays I had attended a series of lectures by Sir Dugald Clerk in one of which he had pointed out the great advantage that might be obtained by operating a petrol engine with stratified charge, as opposed to throttling a homogeneous mixture, but he admitted that he had not yet tried this. … The intention behind the idea was to eliminate the thermo-dynamically wasteful process of throttling and to control the engine wholly by varying the quality of the mixture within the cylinder. The mixture would necessarily be rich close to the sparking plug in order to ensure ignition but successive layers of charge further from the point of ignition would, by some means, be made progressively weaker; hence the term 'stratified'."

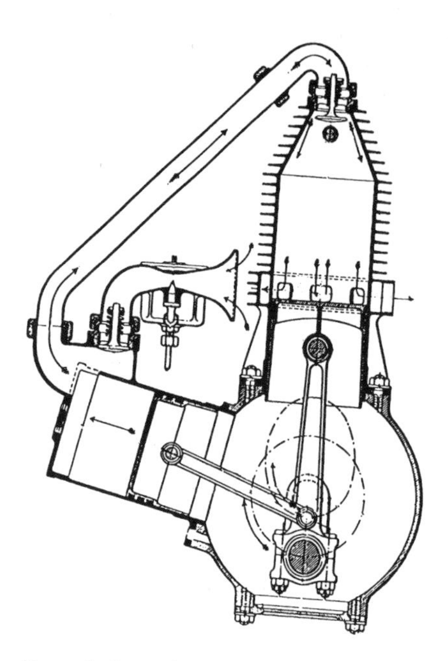

One of the major figures in the internal combustion world when Ricardo was a student was the engineer Sir Dugald Clerk, a prophet of the stratified charge in petrol engines. His aim was to eliminate the thermo-dynamically wasteful process of throttling, and to control the engine wholly by varying the quality of mixture within the cylinder. The mixture was made rich close to the sparking plug, but progressively weaker away from it. The illustration shows Clerk's two-stroke engine. Note additional piston to pump air/fuel mixture into head of cylinder, through the admission valve and past adjacent sparking plug. Exhaust ports are located at bottom of cylinder and exposed by descending piston. This arrangement gave end-to-end scavenging.

Ricardo was already familiar with the workings of the then common stationary gas engine. The Rugby electricity supply came from two Otto-Crossley gas engines, and he later recalled "It is a tribute to their reliability that during the whole five years of my time at Rugby, I cannot recall a single instance of failure of our power supply". A measure of stratification was accomplished in such gas engines by admitting the gas via its own valve into the combustion chamber. Typically, the valve was situated in a pocket at the end of the combustion chamber and this retained a mixture rich enough to allow ignition in the vicinity of the sparking plug or hot tube.

He recalled "It seemed to me that my

engine (the pumping engine), with its conical combustion chamber and central ignition point, would be ideally suited to stratified charge operation and I was determined to try it. I therefore replaced the sparking plug with a small bulb to which I fitted an automatic inlet valve and a sparking plug. I retarded the opening of my main inlet valve so that during the first few degrees of the suction stroke a rich fuel/air mixture would be inhaled into the bulb and thereafter a full charge of air would enter through the mechanically operated inlet valve. ... This arrangement worked perfectly ... the engine ran beautifully, smoothly and quietly over the range of brake mean effective pressures (bmep) from idling to about 15 to 20 pounds per square inch, which was all that I required". He noted "After this I became an enthusiastic advocate of stratified charge operation, for so far it had worked like a charm. It was not until later I discovered its limitations".

Ricardo's next project of relevance to this study was for an automotive engine. He wrote "I had become rather intrigued by the possibilities of ... the two-cycle engine using a separate pumping cylinder as described by Dugald Clerk in his classic book *The Gas and Oil Engine*. Ricardo intended to overcome the tendency of the two-stroke to run erratically at part load – a characteristic that results from the incomplete scavenging of the exhaust gas when the incoming charge is throttled. "Mindful of my experiences with my pumping engine I hoped that ... by employing end-to-end scavenging of the cylinder and by the use of a bulb in the cylinder head through which the in-going mixture would pass ... I would be able to obtain a measure of stratification sufficient to give me good idling".

Since we are discussing mechanical influences here, it is worth noting that end-to-end scavenging of the cylinder using a poppet admission valve and exhaust ports over-run by the piston at the bottom of its stroke resembles, in principle, the system used in the Uniflow steam engine which the young Ricardo had learned of with

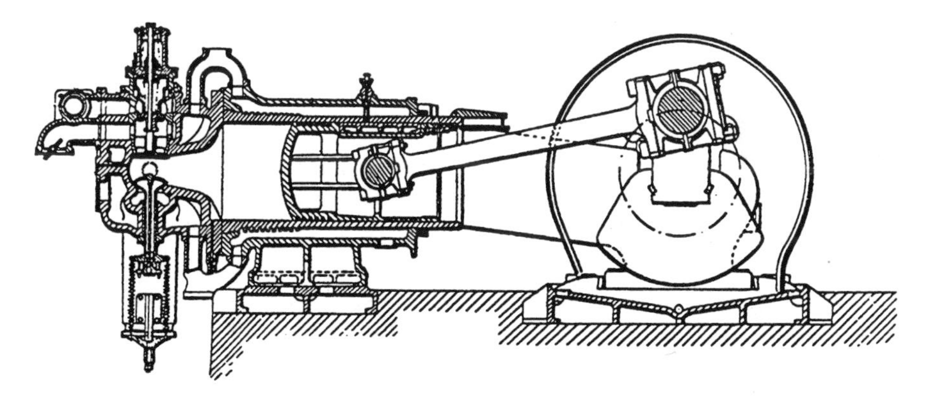

The Otto-Crossley gas engine. The engine sucked a full charge of fresh air at every suction stroke although the gas supply could be reduced to neglible power. The positioning of the admission valve in a pocket at the end of the cylinder retained a relatively rich mixture thus preventing it becoming too weak to run the engine. This technique came to be known as stratified charge. Keep in mind the bell-shaped combustion chamber.

interest; indeed, he had even built an example. "During my years at Rugby ... I heard for the first time of a new form of steam engine known as the 'Uniflow' engine (in which) a very high efficiency was obtained without the need for compounding". We have already noted his interest in those years in the conventional gas engine with its inlet and exhaust valves in a pocket to assist stratification. He also observed that he was impressed by the bulb-headed Hornsby-Ackroyd semi-diesels. All these features, we shall see, recurred in the Crecy story.

The new two-stroke petrol engine Ricardo devised on the Clerk pattern showed some promise, and though not especially powerful, was extremely well-mannered. Christened the 'Dolphin' it was put into production for automobiles in 1906. Only about eight four-cylinder Dolphin cars were made by Ricardo and his partners, but over a hundred Vox light cars were produced by the Lloyd and Plaister company with the basic two-cylinder Dolphin engines built under licence. In addition, the engine proved popular with the fishing fleet at Shoreham, where it was built, for the good low-speed behaviour enabled it to run at a mere 160 rpm when drift-netting.

In essence the Dolphin was typical of the pump-charged two-stroke advocated by Dugald Clerk (and styled by him the 'impulse-every-revolution' engine) though the use of stratification and a bulb head was original. The pump charging was achieved by a second compressor cylinder at 90 degrees to the working cylinder into which it passed the mixture through a manifold. Thus the basic unit had the appearance of a V-twin, although combustion took place only in one cylinder. An incidental advantage is that the system obviates the need for crankcase compression and the use of 'petroil' mixture or a constant-loss oil supply.

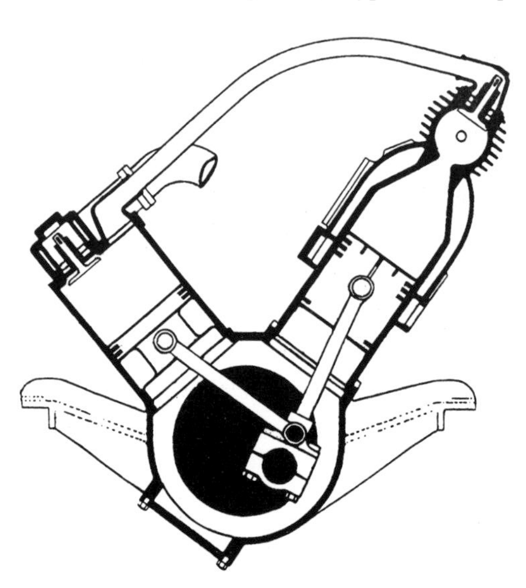

Ricardo employed the stratified charge principle in his Dolphin engine, retaining the rich mixture in a spherical bulb at the apex of the combustion chamber. This engine, though low-powered, ran smoothly and idled very well. With friends, he set up a company at Shoreham in Sussex in 1906 to make Dolphin cars. The engines were also employed by the entire local fishing fleet which, because of the steady low-speed running, proved ideal for drift-netting. The basic unit was a 16 hp V-twin (with one pumping cylinder and one working cylinder) but it was also the basis of a V-4 unit with two working cylinders.

In spite of its modest power this engine is an interesting precursor of the Crecy for most of the distinctive features of the Crecy are seen in the Dolphin. Thus both are two-strokes with a combination of cylinder porting and a mechanically-operated valve giving uniflow scavenge. Both employ an auxiliary compressor for the inlet air, and both have stratification of the charge, using a

The more powerful version of the Dolphin engine with four-cylinders; two pumping cylinders on the right connected by transfer pipes to the two working cylinders on the left. It generated some 30 hp.

bulb-pattern cylinder head.

After leaving Rugby in 1903 Ricardo had gone on to Cambridge. There he studied mechanical engineering with Professor Bertram Hopkinson – an important figure in the development of internal combustion engine science. Ricardo showed great aptitude for experimental internal combustion engineering but little for the formal academic work. With great insight Hopkinson suggested that he give up the course leading to the Honours degree and assist instead in a course of research on the internal combustion engine for which he would receive a 'pass' degree. Hopkinson's programme concerned the limits to power in combustion engines and turned Ricardo's attention particularly to turbulence, temperature gradients within cylinders and 'knock'. Thus Ricardo was set on a path which led to him be coming the most influential British engine consultant. The pursuit of these elusive combustion phenomena was eventually to give Ricardo a firm belief in the sleeve valve and to lead ultimately to the Crecy.

Sleeve valves and two strokes

After Cambridge Ricardo joined the family civil engineering company (Rendel Palmer and Tritton) but continued to work on engine projects, eventually setting up a workshop in the garden of his house at Walton-on-Thames. With typical modesty Ricardo described this as "a large shed in the garden" although it was a quite special facility, for the time, to be devoted to internal combustion work, housing six machinists and fitters and various tools including four lathes, milling machine, drill presses, universal grinder, test engines and two dynamometers. Soon after the outbreak of the First World War Ricardo was drawn into government work, designing an airship engine for the Royal Naval Air Service, (developed to the prototype stage only as the V12-cylinder Ricardo-Halford-Armstrong or RHA) and, more importantly, the 150 hp engine used in the British Mk.V tank, which was manufactured by a consortium of engine builders including Mirrlees, Crossley, Peter Brotherhood and Gardners. Ricardo also continued studying the phenomenon of knock and the influence of the composition of the fuel.

Immediately after the war, he was given a contract from Shell (the Asiatic Petroleum Company, as it then was), to carry on with this work, and he brought into the project two scientists who were to be crucial to the Crecy story. One was Henry Tizard, (to be knighted in 1937) an Oxford physical chemist who during the war had become head of experimental flight testing of aircraft at Martlesham Heath. The other was another physicist, David Pye, who had been scientific adviser on fuels at the Ministry of Munitions, and it is important, for this story, to bear in mind that the three became firm friends.

Between them, these still quite young men explained the mechanism of detonation, or 'knock' in petrol engines and established the principle of knock rating, although they measured the likelihood of a fuel to detonate in terms of a 'toluene number' comparison, until the American octane number system was generally adopted some years later.

A spin-off from this research was a special aromatic fuel made by Shell which allowed the compression ratio of the early Rolls-Royce Eagle to be raised from 5:1 to 6:1 giving 10% more maximum power and 12-15% better economy at cruising speed. This reached the ears of Alcock and Brown who went to Shoreham to learn more about it. The consequence was that Shell agreed to make sufficient for their Atlantic flight.

Ricardo went on to become one of the most eminent and influential internal combustion experts of all time, but there was another element of his research that had a direct bearing on the Crecy internal combustion story – the single-sleeve valve.

Ricardo noted that the Argyll sleeve-valve engine had put up a remarkably fine performance, both in the way of high power and low fuel consumption, in a War Office trial before the First World War. In 1920, when carrying out experiments on combustion chamber shapes he decided to use this type of valve, "not", he said "out of any particular love for this mechanism, but I thought it would give me more freedom of manoeuvre".

It was during the course of research on this unit that he "fell deeply in love with the sleeve-valve, for its own sake. In those days, we had to deal with very inferior fuels, with an octane number of less than sixty, and I was much impressed by the fact that, as compared with our overhead poppet-valve engine, we could employ just one whole ratio higher compression on the same fuel and gain a very big advantage".

The whole move towards sleeve valves in the British aero-engine industry was driven by Ricardo. He recorded "I succeeded in persuading Sir Roy Fedden, of the Bristol Aeroplane Company, to build a complete engine. This, with much misgiving he did". Of course, Fedden became a convert, though many may feel his first misgivings were right. Bristol and Firth-Vickers tried between fifty and sixty compositions of steel, and about 1100 heat treatments to get a sleeve that was right for production, and spent £2 million on the effort. (This figure, incidentally, was approximately twice what the Ministry of Aircraft Production spent in WW II on Whittle and Power Jets to obtain an entirely new prime mover!) Ricardo said of these events "It was perhaps unfortunate that the only firm which was sufficiently interested to take an active part was wedded to air-cooled radial engines" and "that so many years should have elapsed between the completion of the research and its practical development was bitterly disappointing to me; all the more so, since the advantages of the sleeve-valve aero-engine were most apparent in the days when we were using relatively-low-octane fuels".

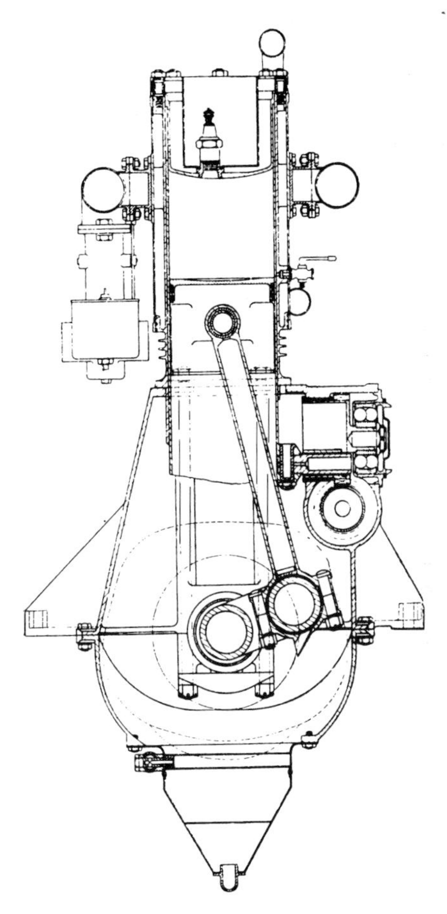

Ricardo was impressed by the high power and low fuel consumption of the Argyll sleeve-valve aero engine (1913). In 1920, when carrying out combustion chamber experiments, he decided to try out this type of valve and as a consequence "fell deeply in love with it". He discovered that, with the inferior fuels of that time, the sleeve-valve allowed him to employ one whole ratio higher compression than was previously permitted with the standard poppet valve.

By the mid-twenties Ricardo's associate in the earlier fuel and knock work, Tizard, had achieved a wide influence on national policy in defence R&D. In particular, he became chairman of the Engine Sub-Committee of the Aeronautical Research Committee (ARC). Ricardo sat on this Committee, as did David Pye who now occupied the important post of Deputy Director of Scientific Research at the Air Ministry. The task of the Committee was, in essence, to direct the course of British aero-engine development, steering the direction of engine research funded by the Air Ministry.

In those inter-war years, the possibilities of the diesel loomed large in their discussions. In part, this was stimulated by the desire to reduce the fire risk in airships. However, the development of diesels with a good enough power-to-weight ratio for aeroplanes was also a priority with the Committee. Ricardo's consultancy was heavily engaged on the problem, while the engine department at the RAE, Farnborough, was largely occupied with diesel work.

At Farnborough, soon after the First World War, it had been decided to build a large diesel single-cylinder research engine for airship use, and although airship research was officially halted there for a time from 1921, the diesel work continued "because the needs of the airship today are the aeroplane needs of the future". This work led to a cylinder designated the RAE 20T which had 8-inch bore, 11-inch stroke and a compression ratio of 12:1, designed to run at 1200 rpm. When the R101 airship project was instigated the Beardmore company was engaged to build the Tornado diesels for it but it appears that the Tornado cylinder design was in fact the RAE 20T.

There are various reasons for this concentration on diesels. The first, as stated, was the fire risk. In 1925, Tizard observed to the Committee that "as the risks of flying become less, those that remained would receive greater prominence, and hence the fire risk with petrol might no longer be tolerated". Another reason was fuel consumption. Imperial air routes needed aircraft with long range, and in 1921 Ricardo's received an Air Ministry contract to investigate all possible means of improving the fuel economy of aero -engines.

An additional reason to favour the diesel, which became more persuasive as petrol engine outputs rose, was 'knock' or detonation. By the late 1920s the power outputs of petrol aero-engines were limited by the low octane number of the fuel available, and as diesels for aviation improved in the laboratories it seemed likely that, being immune to knock, they would soon overtake the petrol engine in terms of specific power. What was not anticipated was the extent to which petrol would be improved and by the time diesel engines had been brought to readiness, octane ratings had increased and the petrol engine sprang ahead again.

One research project was the conversion of two Rolls-Royce Kestrels to diesel operation in 1927-30. This was an Air Ministry contract, carried out in conjunction with Rolls-Royce, but the design and mechanical work was done in Ricardo's laboratory at Shoreham.

The engine used Ricardo's favourite system of single- sleeve valve which ran in new alloy bores in the block replacing the normal wet liners. The dieselised Kestrel, known as the RR/D, was disappointing in that power output was only 350 bhp, the white-metalled big-ends failed, and the forked connecting-rods began to crack. Cracks also started to appear in the cylinder block and there were piston failures. At 820 psi the peak cylinder pressure was too high for the design. However, the RR/D was subsequently bought by the Wakefield Castrol Company on behalf of Captain G E T Eyston and fitted into his car Speed of the Wind (renamed Flying Spray for diesel work) which had already taken many records with a standard Kestrel. The RR/D was set up at Ricardo's to give about 250 bhp and Eyston achieved 159 mph

The Rolls-Royce/Ricardo RR/D Kestrel diesel. The inter-war years saw the rise in prominence of the diesel engine in aviation, initially to reduce the risk of fire, particularly in airships, and for its benefits in fuel economy. By the late 'twenties' the power output of petrol engines was limited by detonation brought on by the low octane rating of the fuels then available. An Air Ministry-sponsored collaboration between Ricardo and Rolls-Royce, the former being chiefly responsible for design and mechanical work, produced two conversions of Kestrel engines to sleeve-valve, diesel operation, known as the Ricardo RR/D engines. The result was relatively disappointing, being of lower power than had been hoped and poor reliability.

at Bonneville Salt Flats in 1936 – a record that was to stand until 1953. This engine is still in existence.

This sleeve-valve work created much interest and the second Rolls-Royce/ Ricardo engine was shipped up to Derby to be converted to petrol operation, partly because the Air Ministry was at that time eager to know whether the advantages claimed by Ricardo for the sleeve-valve would apply in a full-size liquid-cooled petrol engine, and also, as the minutes of the Aeronautical Research Council record, because "Rowledge, Elliott and other Rolls-Royce men were very enthusiastic".

Apparently, the petrol version (known as the RR/P) produced 680 bhp at 3000 rpm, with the standard moderate supercharger – considerably better than the standard engine, although the sleeves blued and the pistons started to overheat. There is no direct evidence but it would not be unreasonable to surmise that this experiment paved the way for the contract subsequently given to Napiers to develop the Sabre.

The disappointing difference in power between the diesel and petrol versions of the Ricardo-modified sleeve-valve Kestrels, combined with their other experimental

The Rolls-Royce/Ricardo RR/P. The second RR/D was converted to petrol operation at the request of the Air Ministry as the fastest way of finding out whether the single-sleeve-valve offered advantages over the poppet valve in a liquid-cooled engine. In a comparison with the RR/D it produced 467 bhp at 2250 rpm as against the latter's 330 bhp. (RR/P powers calculated without supercharger to make comparison fair.) BMEP was 141 lb compared with the latter's 99.5 lb. The RR/P can be distinguished from the RR/D by the distributors mounted at the rear of each cylinder head and the fact that it was supercharged. Both engines featured junkheads to seal the top of the sleeves.

work, now persuaded Ricardo that the two-stroke diesel might have a better chance than the supercharged four-stroke of competing with the petrol engine and he started to advocate this line of development to the ARC Engine Sub-Committee. Since the diesel structure must be built comparatively heavy to cope with the high peak pressures, it makes sense, in the interests of gaining a good power-to-weight ratio, to make the engine two-cycle, for though this path aggravates the heat flow problems of piston and head, it makes more economical use, in a structural sense, of the scantlings and bottom end.

To pursue this, in 1930 Ricardo's designed and built a single-cylinder two-stroke diesel research engine with uniflow scavenge achieved by a sleeve-valve. At a meeting of the Engine Sub-Committee at the Air Ministry in February 1932 Ricardo reported on this work. He pointed out the great asset of the two-stroke cycle from the mechanical design point of view – what he described as the "freedom from the smashing effect of load reversals" – hence the good condition of the big-end and bottom end in his test engine. All Ricardo's information had been communicated to

Rolls-Royce, he reported, to form the basis of a high-performance multi-cylinder engine, Ricardo apparently proposing a sixteen-cylinder unit, with four banks of four cylinders.

There was some note of caution, for Pye pointed out that the single-cylinder engine had needed to be opened up five times in a 68-hour run when a power drop had been seen. However, Pye went on to say that he "had a long discussion with Sir Henry Royce and his staff as to the possible development of the two-stroke compression-ignition engine. Sir Henry Royce agreed to scheme-out engines based on Ricardo's sleeve valve, and the Junkers opposed-piston design".

A little earlier, Pye had reported to the Committee that "when Sir Henry Royce was at Shoreham he appeared to be keener about two-cycle operation than anything else, on account of the reduction in torque variation". According to the Ricardo company, it also appears that Sir Henry Royce discussed the possibility of a 12-cylinder vee two-stroke in 1931 and gave Ricardo some rough schemes to study. West Wittering was only thirty miles from Shoreham and it seems that Harry Ricardo paid frequent social visits there. Royce also visited Shoreham, coming on one occasion to see the RR/D run and shaking hands with all the staff on the testbed.

Ricardo's work, combined with the RAE experiments, succeeded in fostering Royce's enthusiasm for the aero diesel. In February 1931 he wrote to Rowledge and the other senior Company designers from Le Canadel in the south of France where he spent the winters, under the heading 'Compression Ignition ... Suggested letter for Mr Pye'. The discussion is clearly part of the dialogue with Pye and the Air Ministry about the possibility of the Company undertaking diesel work with Ministry support. He noted that "we expected that we should get some results from either the R.A.F.'s Condor or Mr Ricardo's engine made from F engine parts [the Kestrel-based RR/D] that would have given us a very definite indication of the way we ought to proceed with our engine designs and experiments, but to get anything going satisfactorily has taken us much longer than any of us imagined, and still we have nothing to work upon. Owing to many difficulties we could forsee in the practical construction of the sleeve-vale aero engine we decided to try what could be done with our more usual cylinder construction, hoping that the Condor would have provided the necessary information. The experimental work seems easy up to certain standard of efficiency and we get there fairly quickly, after which it is very slow work to get any further".

This is, no doubt, a reference to the relatively modest power output of the RAE compression-ignition Condor. Royce proposed new experiments at Derby dismissing, for the time being, the two-stroke sleeve-valve as promoted by Ricardo, making the interesting observation that "I had the fortune to think of the single-sleeve construction about 1908, the autumn before McCullem's patent, and a year before the Bert patent. My object was to use the same ports for inlet and exhaust and so keep them and the piston rings cool. Now the two-cycle makes this valuable feature impossible and I concluded this might be troublesome in Mr Ricardo's scheme. I do not know if this has been found to be so, but it made me think of the poppet valve for exhaust and the cylinder ports for inlet".

Therefore, Royce proposed "the engine here suggested is not of the sleeve-valve or double-piston type but has a hemispherical head with a group of three or four exhaust valves which open just before the inlet port which is under pressure from the supercharger". However, there was already an experimental diesel cylinder in operation at Derby and he concluded by noting that "perhaps Hives will find much work to do with his special experimental engineer running our unit, which I understand is now fitted up in a test house of its own".

It should be emphasised again how seriously this aeronautical diesel work was being taken at the time. With Ricardo's actively experimenting on the project and the major proportion of the Engine Department at Farnborough also working on compression-ignition, the greatest proportion of the 'advanced projects' type of engine research in Britain was devoted to the aviation diesel.

Thus in 1933 we have Tizard saying to the Committee that "there did not appear to be any engine development so promising as this". In addition to the hoped-for Rolls-Royce involvement a contract had been placed with Bristol for preliminary drawing office work in connection with a radial design. Furthermore, Napier had obtained a licence to build the Junkers diesel (the Culverin) – a developed design that had been proved in aviation service. However, there seemed to be little commercial interest in the diesel and by 1935. Tizard was saying "Somebody in authority must have the courage – or the foolishness – to say we must have the compression-ignition engine".

Diesel cylinders at Ricardo

The type of diesel under investigation by Ricardo at this stage, and on which the Engine Sub-Committee's hopes were based, was a two-stroke sleeve-valve unit (called by them the E.40) in which the sleeve was sealed at the cylinder head by a junkhead, as in Bristol sleeve-valve engines. In this system a cylindrical projection of the cylinder head fitted into the top end of the sleeve and carried piston rings for sealing. However, in the two-stroke diesel, Ricardo noted, these rings were never really trouble free, in spite of their own separate supply of lubricating oil, and were prone to gumming and carbon deposition which rendered them inoperative. Therefore, "it was decided to attempt the bold experiment of abolishing the head rings altogether and exhausting over the top edge of the sleeve.... The cylinder head simply became a lid containing the combustion chamber".

It was first imagined that the top of the sleeve needed to be thinned down almost to a knife edge to allow it sufficient flexibility under gas pressure to seal against the wall of the bore. Subsequent experience showed this to be unnecessary. The sleeve clearance was, to a certain extent, self regulating, for the sleeve would expand thermally until it had sufficient contact with the bore wall to stabilise the heat flow, and in this condition gas sealing was satisfactory. This feature, called by Ricardo the 'open-ended sleeve' was described by the company as "a real breakthrough".

A more sophisticated Ricardo diesel design, the E.44, then followed incorporating the open-ended sleeve. It had a 5-inch bore and 5.5-inch stroke and ran at 2500 rpm, generating outputs which Ricardo was able to extrapolate to support his claim that the two-stroke diesel would be able to equal or exceed the output of the current four-stroke petrol engine. An engine of Kestrel size, he suggested, could be made in diesel form at about 1.5 lb per horsepower, yeilding a take-off power of 660 bhp, although he also predicted rather earlier that it could achieve 735 bhp.

Rolls-Royce and the diesel

The role of Rolls-Royce and its relationship with the Air Ministry over diesel work during the early 1930s is enigmatic. We know of the contacts between Ricardo and both Derby personnel and Sir Henry Royce and the expressions of interest in the diesel from the Company. However, no serious design work seems to have been undertaken and in September Royce wrote again to Rowledge and Hives about diesel work in obvious frustration. He complained; "We are not making sufficient progress and we are on the way towards missing our chance. My impression is that this type of engine is of the utmost importance to us within the next few years. Every motor boat owner , and all aeroplane pilots would welcome enormously the absence of highly volatile inflammable fuel. One cannot imagine civil aviation going on without this type of engine. Our aero engine position is precarious unless we keep right in front. The proposed piston engine is not, to my mind, any good, and even with supercharging all the efforts we have in hand are 'so-so' – i.e. not bad, but not good enough. I have visited Mr Ricardo and seen his RR-Ricardo engine made from Kestrel parts running, probably the best attempt that we know, but even Mr Ricardo doubts if it is good enough to be really useful, even if supercharged".

In 1930, Rolls-Royce was running a single-cylinder, compression-ignition engine of 6-inch bore, 8-inch stroke. Compression ratio was 14.2:1. This unit had poppet valves of which the inlet was fitted with a deflector to promote swirl. Fuel was injected by a Bosch pump.

Royce now abandoned his earlier suspicion of the two-stroke sleeve-valve diesel, proposing that "the single-sleeve valve is the way to make a trial, although we have done some work with poppet valves", and continuing "Mr Ricardo's scheme for compression-ignition work has many merits, some of which I had not realised".

In spite of the earlier discussion of the involvement of Pye and the Air Ministry in sponsoring diesel work finacially, Royce now noted that "it is understood that the Government will not agree or subscribe towards any of this experimental work. Personally I am not sorry because if they did the results would not be exclusively ours, as I very much wish, but we also think that as soon as we get started the Ministry will get interested and would pay any ordinary bill". However, a few months later, in 1932, Pye reported

'P SLEEVE-VALVE PETROL-INJECTION KESTREL

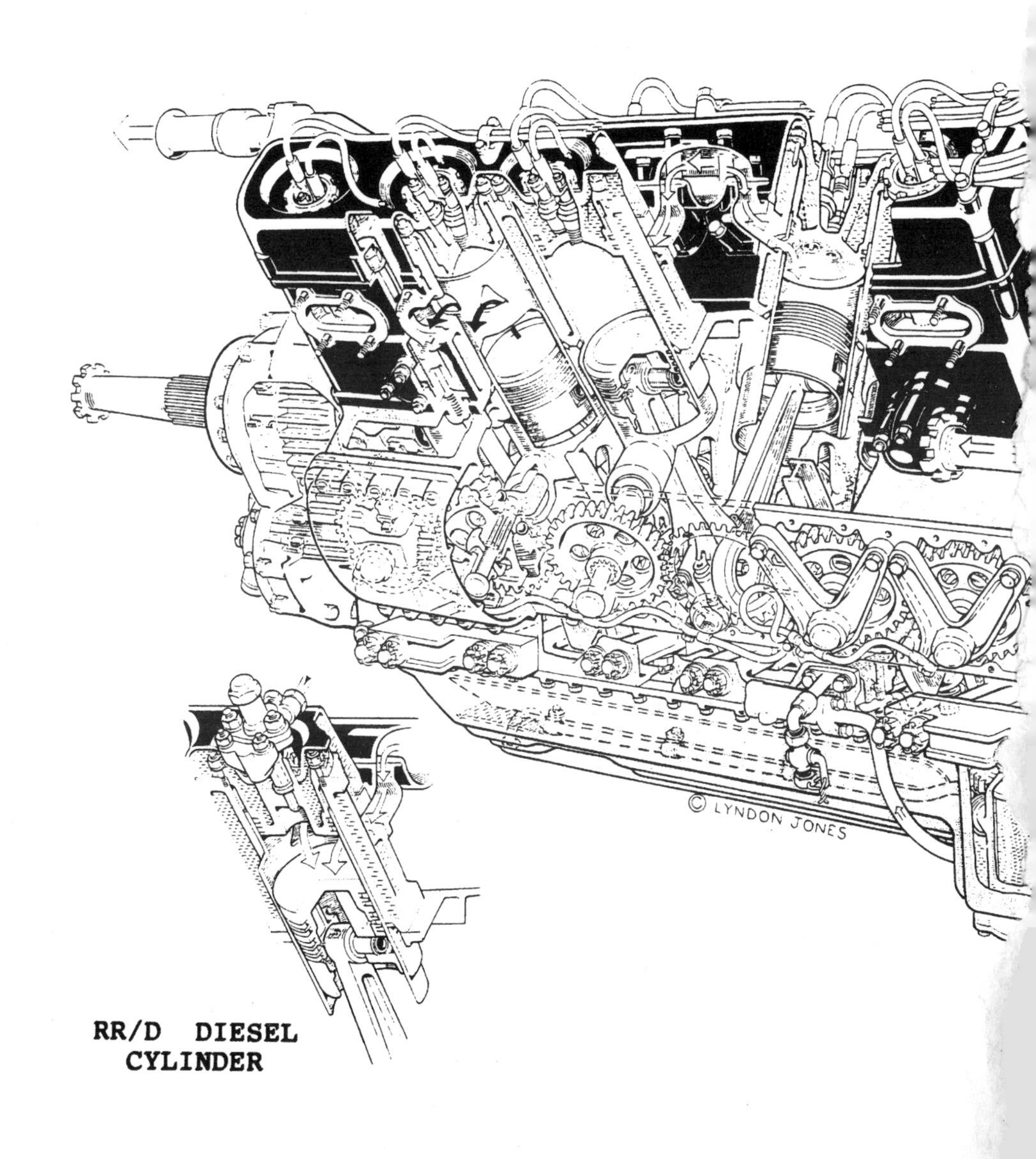

RR/D DIESEL
CYLINDER

ROLLS-ROYCE - RIC

that he "had a long discussion with Sir Henry and his staff" about the Ricardo-pattern two-stroke and, in his role as Deputy Director of Scientific Research (DDSR) at the Air Ministry, asked the Company to scheme out an engine.

The resulting design (which presumably was done under Rowledge's supervision) offered a maximum net output of 540 bhp with economical cruising power of 470-490 bhp from a V-12 two-stroke layout. This seemed, to the Engine Sub-Committee, "unattractive" since the output was much worse than that promised by Ricardo.

Rolls-Royce then amended the design scheme to offer 640 bhp and this was given grudging encouragement by the Engine Sub-Committee, " as a way of keeping Rolls-Royce interested in compression-ignition" but support for the project was in fact refused in May 1933 by the special panel of the Engine Sub-Committee set up to study the aero diesel.

For this reason, perhaps, the diesel engine expertise at Derby was strengthened in the next year by the recruitment of Harry Wood. Wood had been an engineer fitter apprentice at the Royal Naval Dockyard at Sheerness between 1906 and 1912 where, one might guess, he had contact with diesels in submarine use. In 1915 he moved to the Royal Aircraft Establishment at Farnborough to work on aero engines and began the conversion of the Rolls-Royce Condor there to diesel operation. Between 1928 and 1931 he was sent to the Royal Airship Works at Cardington to work on the Beardmore diesel units for the R101 before moving to the technical development section in the Air Ministry. Not surprisingly, perhaps, Ernest Hives (then Head of the Experimental Department at Rolls-Royce) had previously met Wood for when he toured the engine department at Farnborough in 1931 it was Wood who showed him around.

In November 1937 Wood produced a Rolls-Royce paper "to examine the aircraft prospects of the CI [compression-ignition] engine in view of the advance in performance of the current supercharged 87-octane fuel and the further advances anticipated from the introduction of 100-octane fuel". He concluded that since the same brake mean effective pressure was theoretically attainable from both types of engine the diesel could compete, although he noted that the diesel would require 20% more boost air. Perhaps paradoxically, he also observed that "the greater blower powers required for a CI engine means that for a given shaft horsepower the CI cylinders will be carrying a higher load". This, of course, had been the nub of all aero diesel work and Wood's paper, although encouraging from an airflow and thermodynamic viewpoint, did not address the implications of this higher load on mechanical design and structure weight.

Thus Rolls-Royce kept a foot in diesel work, though whether this was done through Air Ministry research contracts or on the Company's own initiative is not known. When the two new Ricardo E.44 two-stroke test engines were built, one of them incorporated many parts machined at Derby for Ricardo. Possibly this was an informal arrangement for when Rolls-Royce formally asked the Air Ministry in 1937 for permission to build a complete E.44 to run at Derby permission was delayed for several months. Hives (now General Works Manager) was forced to apologise, writing in uncharacteristically humble vein in 1938 to the Air Ministry that "there is one point where I am afraid we have gone wrong. We want very badly

The compression-ignition Rolls-Royce Condor engine installed in Hawker Horsley J8003 at RAE Farnborough which flew in November 1932 piloted by S/Ldr Caster, with Andrew Swan of the RAE as observer. The engine was a disappointment and in comparison with the standard Condor produced only 560 bhp as opposed to the latter's 790. BMEP was also down, from 139 lb to 98.8. Fuel consumption was slightly higher. The first diesel-powered aircraft flight in the world was accomplished in the USA in September 1928 with a Stinson aircraft powered by a Packard air-cooled radial diesel. The prototype opposed-piston Junkers diesel was first flown in 1929.

to know whether or not the expansion sleeve [Hives' term for the Ricardo open-ended sleeve, also sometimes called at Rolls-Royce the self-sealing sleeve] is satisfactory; we have talked to Mr Ricardo and he has given us a certain amount of encouragement, but we think the decision is so important and so fundamental in laying out a new design of engine that we shall not be satisfied until we have run tests ourselves at Derby with an engine having this sleeve construction. I conceived the idea that the quickest way to get this result was to make a duplicate engine to the one Ricardo has running. .... I am afraid I overlooked the question that the design of this unit was the property of the Air Ministry. .... For this I apologise, but I would be grateful if you would give your permission that we can have the drawings, so that we can proceed with the unit".

This state of affairs certainly seems odd, particularly in view of the earlier ARC desire to keep Rolls-Royce "interested in compression-ignition". Neither does the problem seem to have originated with any commercial jealousy at Ricardo for their account noted that towards the end of 1937 "Rolls-Royce had definitely decided they ought either to build an E.44 for their own use or to get us to build one for them. Then came a delay.... as the Air Ministry would not give us permission to pass on our information to Derby. .... This was the more inexplicable as many components of our second E.44 had been made at Derby, where there were of course copies of the relevant drawings".

By 11 February 1938 (in view of the international situation rather late in the day, one might think, for diesel work to be still in train) Hives wrote to Pye at the Air Ministry noting that "Mr Wood was relieved of all other duties to enable him to look into the C I engine position. Mr Rowledge has also given a considerable amount of time recently to this problem. After carefully considering the whole position, we have decided that we should go into the development and production of a CI engine; at the same time we are conscious of the fact that although Bristols, Siddeleys, Napiers and Rolls-Royce have each in the past carried out considerable development work in connection with compression-ignition at DSR expense, there is very little to show for it in the form of a satisfactory CI aircraft engine".

Hives continued "I do not share the optimism which you may have read into Wood's reports. .... The picture I see of the CI engine until we know a lot more about it is that it is going to weigh more and give less power than the equivalent petrol aero engine".

Hives spelled out the approach he recommended which typified his marvellous pragmatic sense for engineering development. "The policy I advocate whenever tackling a new problem is to keep the problem as simple as possible, and I submit that to tackle the CI engine on the basis of competing with the latest aircraft petrol engines makes the job much too difficult. We have therefore come to the conclusion that to give the CI engine a chance, and to make the problem as simple as possible, the most satisfactory way to develop the ultimate aircraft CI engine is by starting off with one for marine work.

I consider the aircraft constructors have been spoiled in as much that every year they have been given increased powers out of the same engines, and I can find no enthusiasm among aircraft constructors when you suggest a CI engine which may give less performance than the equivalent petrol engine. The marine man, however, is absolutely enthusiastic .... in spite of it being slightly larger, slightly heavier and less powerful than the latest petrol-type engines".

Hives went on to set out the advantages, including that of being relieved of the problem of power at high altitude and of providing special high take-off power, suggesting that this would be the quickest way to arrive at the best CI engine for aircraft. "There is also the psychological effect", he suggested. "One might make a perfectly good CI engine; in fact the best in the world, yet it might still not be appreciated by the aircraft people; whereas if one could make a reliable CI engine for marine work, weighing, say 1500 lb, approx. per 1000 hp, one can foresee an immediate demand".

A successful marine engine, Hives argued, would build experience and "give us a chance to put the CI engine on a commercial footing to enable us to carry the necessary specialists". Then, he argued, "it would not be long before a competitive CI engine would be available for aircraft".

The Air Ministry appears to have concurred with this, perhaps simply as a way of keeping research going on the single-sleeve valve two-stroke, for as we shall see, by 1938 the ARC and the Air Ministry were no longer really interested in the E.44-type diesel for its own sake, but as the mechanical basis for a quite new type of petrol engine – an extremely high-performance fighter engine conceived for the needs of the coming air war. However, the relationship between Rolls-Royce and the Air Ministry and ARC Engine Sub-Committee did not seem to improve much on the diesel question. The requests for access to the drawings had been delayed and when, in March 1938, Rolls-Royce asked for the ARC to arrange for endurance tests of the expansion (or 'self-sealing') sleeve to be carried out at Shoreham by Ricardo, W S Farren (now DDSR) replied that he expected "Ricardo will feel that the cylinder in its present form will not stand up to the endurance tests which you propose". The suggested series of 5 ten-hour non-stop runs at "110 bmep" and 2500 rpm, with two hours non-stop at "120 bmep" (the maximum then attainable) were more the "run and bust" development philosophy of Rolls-Royce than the experimental approach of Ricardo. Hives also wrote to Major G P Bulman, in charge of engine procurement for the Royal Air Force, complaining of "the way this job is dragging on. .... The last thing that happened is that we had a visit from Griffith of the RAE [the gas turbine pioneer, later of Rolls-Royce] who asked to call in to go over our CI proposals. We are naturally always pleased to see Griffith and have a talk to him, but if he is another member of a committee to decide if we are sensible or capable, then we shall not get very far".

Finally, on 11 March Farren wrote agreeing to Ricardo supplying the necessary drawings. Just a month later Hives replied "you will be interested to hear that we have completed the two-stroke unit from Ricardo's drawings and it is now being installed on the testbed".

Diesel to petrol – a change of direction

The curious relationship between Rolls-Royce and the ARC over the diesel issue was perhaps a normal state of affairs between the Air Ministry and its major suppliers in the period. However, it may also be that the ARC wished to preserve secrecy over an aspect of the project and to ensure that the Company was on the right track without disclosing fully its ultimate intentions. This can be traced back to 1935 when a remarkable change of direction was suggested for the E.44 two-stroke sleeve-valve diesel project. By that date Ricardo's advocacy of this engine type had been broadly accepted in the ARC and the major aero engine makers were all, to some extent, involved in diesel studies. But in the Engine Sub-Committee, during the meeting of December 1935, something rather strange occurred for the subject of a 'sprint' engine was suddenly raised, for the very first time, by Tizard.

"The Chairman remarked that if it was the desire of the Air Ministry to develop a type of sprint engine for home defence.... there was the question as to how far fuel consumption could be disregarded. Mr Ricardo has raised this point in a recent conversation by enquiring whether a high fuel consumption might not be permissible under certain circumstances, for if so, an investigation of the possibilities of the two-stroke petrol engine appeared to be attractive".

Two months later Ricardo submitted a report to the Committee, which marks the formal beginning of all the Crecy work, entitled Report on High-Power, Two-Cycle Engine for Special Purpose Machines. It starts; "The present note relates to the possibility of developing a special-purpose aero-engine of very high performance for short flights only, without the usual regard for fuel or oil consumption, but in which high specific output and small frontal area are taken as being the dominating conditions".

The proposal was for a petrol development of the Ricardo E.44 diesel two-stroke sleeve-valve unit, adapted to spark-ignition, but still with direct fuel-injection. It is essential to realise that this engine concept, which was eventually to be given the name Crecy , was simply a petrol conversion of the high-power diesel scheme that Ricardo had been developing and promoting over several years to try and make the diesel the equal of the conventional aero engine. When the need for sheer power became apparent the diesel element was dropped, but all the design strategies which had been developed to try and wring a competitive performance from the diesel were kept to contribute to a sprint engine – a pure 'hot-rod' unit for interceptor fighters in which fuel consumption would be regarded as unimportant, and was expected to be poor. So alike were the projects, in fact, that E.44 units were converted directly to the new single-cylinder petrol test units, designated E.65. A new cylinder head was designed to carry the sparking plugs and the injector, and the compression ratio was lowered to 7:1.

David Pye, in the discussion, baulked at the problems of developing a two-stroke and perceptively suggested that the heat flow per cylinder might impose a limit to power. He believed that the use of alcohol fuel in a four-stroke at higher speed – 4000 to 5000 rpm - posed less formidable R&D problems. However, Ricardo's argument was that the mechanical problems with cylinders of one-litre capacity, at the speeds and working pressures Pye envisaged, were not known. With the two-stroke, the inertia of reciprocating parts is balanced by gas pressure and there is a reduction of load reversals and stress particularly on the big-end bearings and crankshaft bearings.

But how did this mysterious proposal come about? The Sub-committee records do not help, but a glance at developments in another area of defence technology will provide a clue.

In January 1935 another committee had been formed in response to the build-up of German military power, with the hope that a way might be found to prevent the bomber "always getting through". This was the Committee for the Scientific Survey of Air Defence. The chairman and leading light of this was, again, Henry Tizard, and it is better known simply as the Tizard Committee. It has often been recounted how one of the first things considered by the Committee was Robert Watson-Watt's analysis of the 'Death Ray' proposal, and his counter suggestion for 'The detection of aircraft by radio methods'.

In February 1935, a van containing a suitable radio receiver was halted about ten miles from the powerful short-wave transmitters of the BBC Daventry broadcasting station, and a radio echo was successfully detected from an aircraft which had been directed to fly through the beam. The Tizard defence committee took great comfort from this demonstration, and suggested that "within five years at the most, it would be able to set interceptor fighters onto all aircraft at 60-100 miles from the coast". But the pace of development was rather faster than this. Within the year, the radar team at Orfordness were able to detect aircraft eighty miles away and the Air

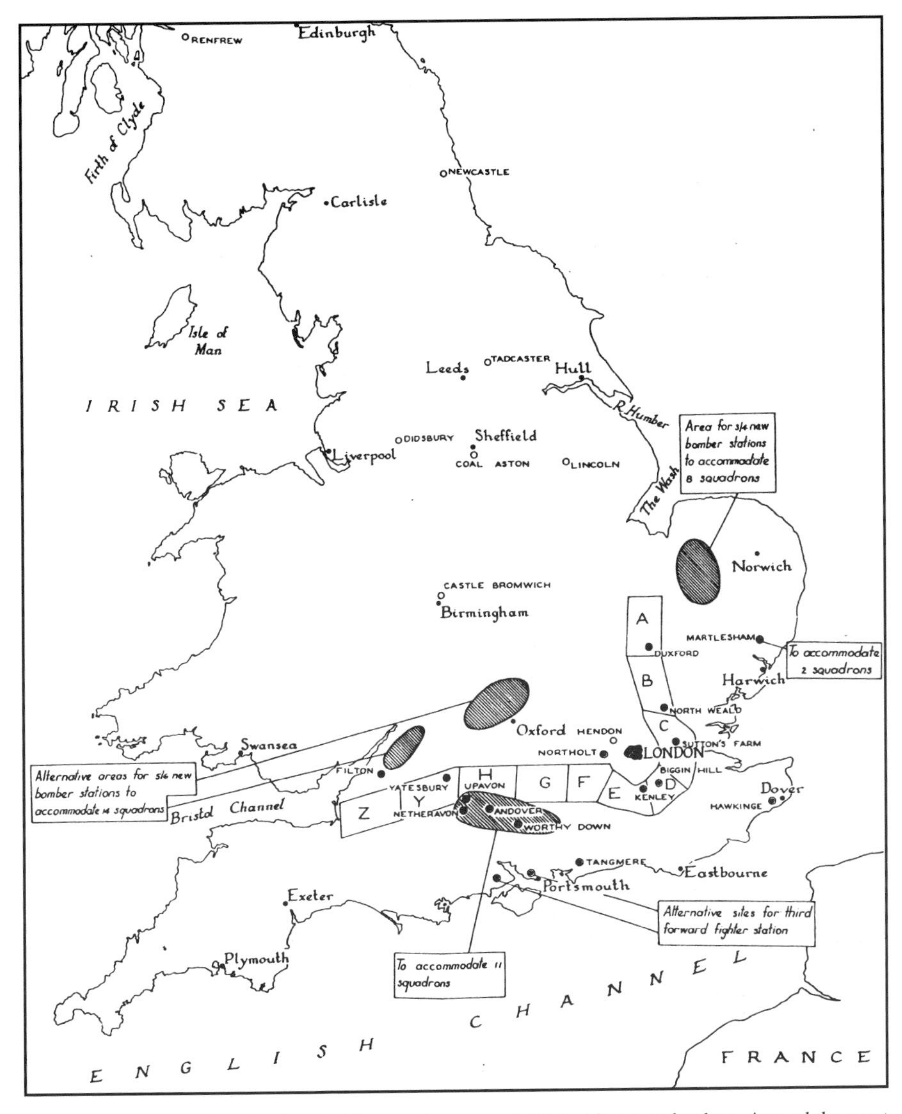

The air fighting map showing the air defence scheme as established in pre-radar days. Around the coast were artillery zones with box areas A to Z designated as aircraft fighting zones each manned by one or more squadrons. These areas were host to aircraft on standing patrol, ready at height. The introduction of radar detection rendered this operation obsolete as aircraft had sufficient warning to climb to interception height when called.

Council had decided to build the Chain Home stations in the South East without delay.

The air defence scheme as established in pre-radar days consisted of coastal artillery zones and aircraft fighting zones, each manned by one or more squadrons. Advanced warning would be give by sound-location equipment and observers in the outer ring, but reliance really had to be placed on mounting standard patrols of aircraft in their sectors, ready at height. These patrols would be relieved periodically as their fuel became exhausted. Obviously only a small proportion of the defending force could be in the air at any one time. But with radar, fighters could be husbanded on the ground, climbing to interception when called.

So, at the end of 1935 Tizard was in an almost unique position. He both knew the potential of radar and was also deeply involved in the direction of research and development on powerplants. It should not be forgotten, too, that he had been in the Royal Flying Corps and had directed the Aeroplane Experimental Station at Martlesham Heath in 1918. This knowledge, it is suggested, must have caused Tizard to discretely encourage his friend Ricardo, at one of their frequent social meetings, to consider the problem of the sprint engine for a radar-directed fighter, in advance of the Engine Sub-Committee meeting when the proposal so abruptly popped up. And though the author has no record of such a thing, there is an example, from exactly the same time, of the way Tizard worked behind the scenes and of his influence on a project for another high-performance engine – one which also was expected to have poor fuel consumption.

Sir Henry Tizard, Chairman of the Aeronautical Research Council, 1933-1943. Was his knowledge of radar, along with matters concerning engine research and development, and his previous involvement with aeronautics, the inspiration behind a sprint engine for radar-controlled fighters?

Hayne Constant, the architect of the early British axial-flow turbojet recalled: "I remember a conversation with (the then) Mr Tizard, the Rector of the Imperial College, in which he asked me what was the most worthwhile research to be done in the engine field. I told him of my hopes of the turbine and he gave an encouraging reply. There is no doubt in my mind that it was Tizard's imagination and enthusiasm that provided the drive during these critical days". Whittle, too, had the same experience and recorded: "Our best friend was Henry Tizard". It was Tizard who made the connections that led to Air Ministry funding of Power Jets.

So these events put the Crecy project in a slightly different light. It was not some 'oddball' project, devised merely to investigate a remote possibility. It was put in hand virtually simultaneously with the gas turbine at a time of great threat, and together these two new types of engine

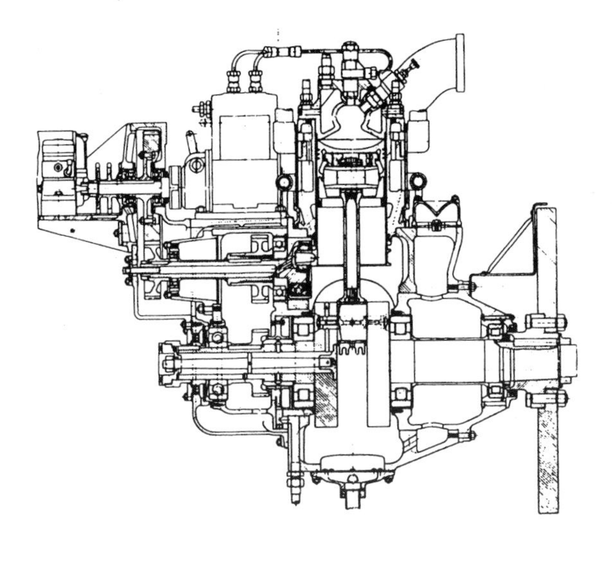

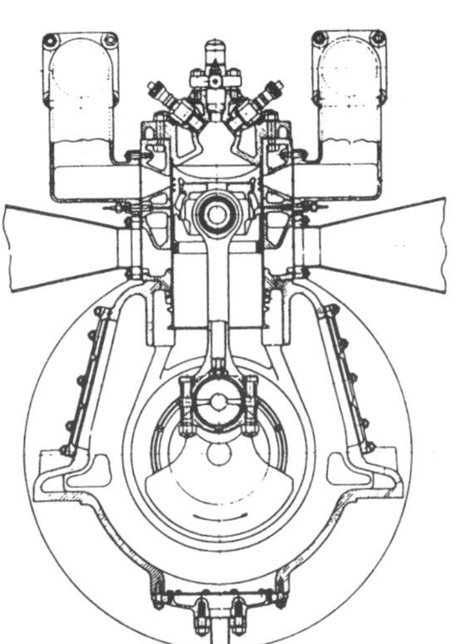

Cross-sectional views of Ricardo's E.65 single-cylinder, sleeve-valve, petrol-injection engine, converted from the E.44 diesel unit. This engine, seen here in its later form, has a number of features later seen in the Crecy such as a bulb head and a sleeve without exhaust ports. Scavenge air was provided from an external source. Cylinder capacity was 1.64 litres.Main dimensions of the unit (with those of the larger E.54 in brackets) were: cylinder bore 5.01 (5.34) inches, sleeve bore 4.81 (5.10) inches, piston stroke 5.5 (6.5) inches, piston swept volume 1639 (2177) cubic centimeters, sleeve stroke 1.5 (1.75) inches, compression ratio 7:1. The combustion chamber capacities for the E.65 were: head bulb 65cc, head cone 80cc, piston cavity 100cc. Throat was diameter 1.5 inches.

represented the best efforts of the defence planners to encourage the development of power units that were suited to the new 'reactive' age of air defence. Clearly it was perceived to be a most important project. Goaded on by an official requirement, development work on the single-cylinder units moved into high gear.

Aero-engine development in the great days of piston engines usually started with a design for a single-cylinder test unit. Early development work on performance, scavenging, heat flow, durability and so on would be done on this test engine, and if results were encouraging, the separate mechanical engineering problem of creating an entire engine with a number of such cylinders would be undertaken. The Ricardo E.65 would be the basis for this single-cylinder research.

By 1938, Ricardo reported the surprising finding that fuel and oil consumption was not as high as had been expected. Their report reads: "From the first, the engine gave a lower fuel consumption and was far less sensitive to the time or manner of injection than was expected. Its running was remarkably smooth, and, in general, its behaviour was in every way most encouraging. It may even be that, for high outputs, the two-stroke can compete with the four-stroke in fuel economy, the greater blower loss being offset by the higher permissible compression ratio and by improved mechanical efficiency of the engine itself".

Mechanically, too, the engine seemed surprisingly trouble-free. "The piston keeps remarkably cool" they reported, "and the bearings have given no trouble of any

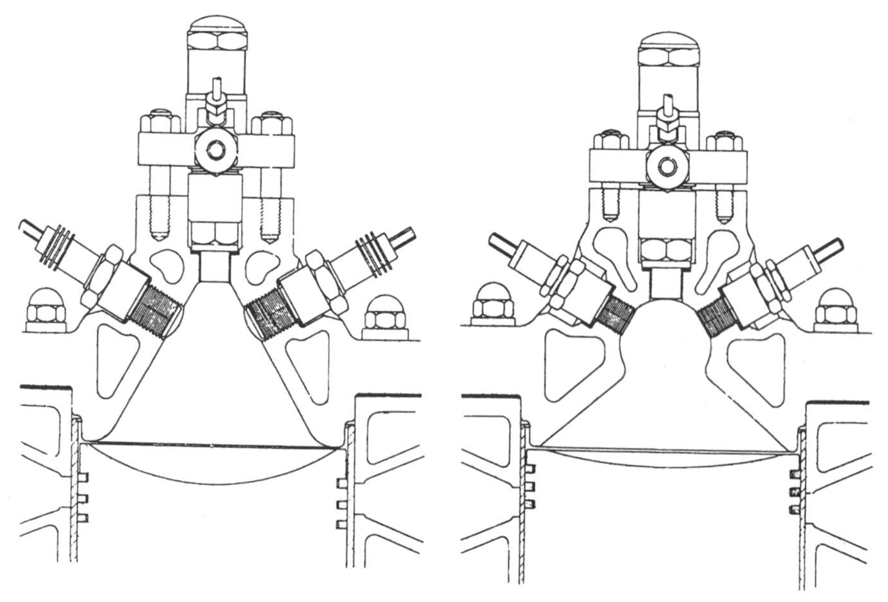

Two head designs evaluated on the E.65 engine by Ricardo. The original (No.1) head featured a straight cone, but to extend the stable burning range to weaker mixtures some means of retaining a rich mixture around the plug had to be devised. This was achieved with the No.4 head with its bulbous chamber atop the now-wider-angle cone.

kind .... mechanical troubles have been practically non-existent". The one-litre single-cylinder unit soon achieved a power output of 100 bhp, and by the following year was delivering 145 gross hp with some 6.5 lb/sq.in scavenge pressure provided by an independent blower.

The role of Rolls-Royce in this period is not clear. A Ministry historical paper written later in the war noted that running of the E.65 "was so successful that the firms of Rolls-Royce, Napier, and Bristol were asked whether they were willing to initiate development work on units and engines based on the E.65 design". The Bristol Aeroplane Co. was too fully occupied to entertain the proposal. Rolls-Royce agreed in December 1938 to co-operate, but withdrew their agreement in January 1939. Napiers agreed to take up the project and a contract was issued for the supply of the first Napier twin-cylinder unit in July 1939.

The Ministry paper went on: "The results obtained on the Ricardo E.65 units had continued to improve and the fuel consumptions were not high as had been expected. On the outbreak of war, in September 1939, Rolls-Royce were again pressed to undertake the work of developing a two-stroke petrol engine as an urgent wartime project and consented to do so. The termination of research on compression-ignition engines enabled the firm to commence work with great rapidity and running on a two-stroke, compression-ignition twin-cylinder unit, converted to petrol-injection and spark-ignition, commenced in January 1940".

It would be interesting to have some confirmation of this account from the Rolls-Royce side, but there apparently is none. Correspondence between Hives and Pye reveal that Rolls-Royce were made aware of the idea of changing the diesel to a sprint engine using petrol injection at the beginning of 1939. In February Pye, who had become Director of Scientific Research, wrote to Hives; "with reference to our discussion yesterday about the development of the sleeve-valve two-stroke petrol engine, I understand you are very anxious to try out the full possibility of this as a very high-output engine. You are already acquainted with the type of cylinder on which very high outputs have been obtained by Ricardo....". (The letter is annotated "Wd – Please see me, Hs".)

This background explains the statement that is often made that "the Crecy was originally intended to be a diesel", but it is also apparent that the history is more complex. In April 1939 Wood issued a specification for a two-stroke marine engine which was a "conversion of the RR.32 CI two-stroke aero-engine". Plainly, this has to be the so-called 'diesel Crecy' and proves that such an engine was schemed if not actually designed. The engine is described as a two-stroke with twelve cylinders forming a 90-degree vee. It was water-cooled and had a 5.6-inch bore and 6.6-inch stroke giving 31.9 litres capacity. There is no mention of sleeves in the brief description but we can surmise that it was based on the Ricardo E.44 cylinder. The link between this engine and the Crecy is the 90-degree cylinder bank configuration, which was a break from the Company's traditional 60-degree layout for its V-12 engines. With respect to the petrol development Wood had already written to the Air Ministry on 10 February 1939 setting out Rolls-Royce proposals for the petrol-injection work stating that "we propose to put in hand the design of a 12-cylinder engine of 5-inch bore and 5.5-inch stroke in order to investigate the main engine problems of performance, reliability, control and manufacture".

Wartime development

The story of the engine concept in its definitive form – as the Rolls-Royce Crecy – will be reviewed by Dick Foster-Pegg in the next chapter, but it is worth discussing, in this account, some facets of the general progress of E.65 research during the war.

The proposed engine was a 'petrolised' diesel – a cocktail of exotic features which had never before been combined in a petrol engin e (and have not been since). To recapitulate, these were two-stroke operation, uniflow scavenge by a single-sleeve valve, direct petrol injection into the cylinder, high supercharge and the

The successful running of the E.65 prompted a Ministry invitation to Rolls-Royce, Napier and Bristol to develop engines along the sa me lines. This was taken up by Napier who produced a twin-cylinder unit to their own design, the E.113. The unit seen in the pictures featured a junkhead and had the bore and stroke of the Sabre engine. It was the basis of a 24-cylinder, X-configuration engine, the programme of which was dropped in January 1942.

intention to use stratified charge for power control to avoid the pumping losses associated with throttling. As encouraging results came through from Ricardo and as the likelihood of war increased, enthusiasm grew at the Air Ministry for two-stroke development but this work appeared to be dragging at Rolls-Royce for Pye wrote to Hives in May 1939, three months before the outbreak of war, saying "I was surprised and disappointed to learn recently that you had not been getting on with the two-stroke petrol-injection project, as was agreed during our discussion at Derby on Feb. 1st". Hives replied that "the position is not anything like as bad as you imagine", but a few weeks later he confessed "we have come up against some very real difficulties with the expansion sleeve and we have decided to produce further units with the junkhead". Pye was uneasy and replied "I remember well that we were all.... very delighted when it was found possible to work with the expanding sleeve, and thought it would mean an all-round improvement in power and endurance. .... In the meantime I must consider what other possibilities there are for the development of a petrol two-stroke based on the Ricardo results with the expanding sleeve".

Whether this veiled threat to place the development contract elsewhere was the reason, or whether, with accumulated experience, the open-ended sleeve started to recommend itself to Rolls-Royce, is not known. Certainly there was no more discussion of junkheads between the Ministry and Rolls-Royce although the engine schemed out by Napier to use the E.65 cylinder was to have a junkhead with piston-type sealing rings, and the Air Ministry supported this as an insurance against any fundamental problems occurring with the open-ended sleeve. This Napier unit was to be, like the Sabre, a 24-cylinder liquid-cooled engine, and was intended to give 3000 bhp at the ambitious speed of 4000 rpm. The Napier Company, deeply troubled by the Sabre development, dropped all petrol two-stroke work in October 1942 and the twin-cylinder engines were transferred to Ricardo. A 1941 report notes that "already trouble has been experienced with head sealing rings despite the comparatively small amount of running", apparently bearing out Ricardo's doubts about the durability of the junkhead arrangement in these high-power two-strokes.

The Ricardo company, incidentally, was moved from its Shoreham works in June 1940 as provision had been made to flood the Adur valley as part of the invasion defences. The company set up research facilities in the University's Engineering School at Norham Gardens in Oxford, also taking over part of a nearby theological college and Hartwell's Garage in South Parade. There they ran five engines; their own two E.65 units, the Rolls-Royce-built V-twin (operated in single-cylinder form and called by them the RR/4), the Napier unit and a Ricardo E.54, built to replicate the Crecy bore and stroke and featuring, for the first time, the sleeve drive from the crankshaft web. These test engines were mounted in a cast-iron cradle which was, in turn, fitted into a five-ton universal cast-iron testbed, and were coupled to a Heenan and Froude water brake. In spite of this massive installation Ricardo's noted that "owing to the nature of the foundations in the laboratory at Oxford it was not possible to run the units at speeds in excess of 2800 rpm without causing very severe vibration", and the very high power tests alluded to later in this book were done after the return to Shoreham at the end of the war.

Meanwhile, the Ministry of Aircraft Production (MAP) was becoming increasingly enthusiastic about the two-stroke and in 1941, according to a Ricardo account, asked Bristol and Armstrong Siddeley to try it again. The reason for this urgent desire to extend two-stroke work was that Ricardo was reporting excellent results from the E.65 units, while performance calculations by government scientists at the RAE, Farnborough on hypothetical aircraft installations were highly encouraging, (see Appendix I).

Part of the reason for the special promise of the engine was its huge throughput of air. The engine was, of course, highly supercharged both for power and to ensure a thorough scavenge or 'blow-down' of exhaust products. In addition the two-stroke has twice the number of exhaust periods of the four-stroke and, potentially a greater net airflow. The efficient utilisation of the energy from the exhaust promised the recovery of much of the work expended in supercharging. The simplest solution was to use the exhaust as a propulsive jet, although the exhaust noise was so high that some wondered if it might be unsuitable even for specialised military duties. (This was a result both of the very rapid opening of the exhaust ports and the fact that, relative to a four-stroke, this event occurred while the cylinder gases were still at high pressure.) However, at high speeds the potential of this jet thrust element

The first of the Rolls-Royce V-twin engines, seen here operating as a diesel. It was subsequently converted to petrol-injection. There were eight such engines at Derby, Shoreham and Farnborough employed on the CI/PI/Crecy programme. The siamesed exhaust pipes are seen rising away from the unit.

became of great importance, for it helped to offset the reduced efficiency of the propellor. The high airflow through the engine also suggested the possibility of exhaust turbocharging – a proposal which originated in late 1939 or early 1940 from A A Griffith who was reported to be working on an "exhaust fan .... very similar to that required". The desire to follow this approach was strengthened by Ricardo's finding that the engine was very tolerant of exhaust back pressure, which had little effect on performance or on heat losses, which were mainly determined by fuel supply.

RAE studies also uncovered a surprising facet of the two-stroke, not dreamed of in the original pre-war sprint engine proposal – a good fuel consumption at high power outputs. A report in September 1942 (by R Smelt and A W Morley) compared the two-stroke with the gas turbine for a six-cannon fighter of two-hour and four-hour endurance. The calculations showed that "a good deal of the advantage of the two-stroke was found to lie in the recovery of additional supercharger work in exhaust thrust; and it is clear that the conditions under which the engine appears most promising will be the same as those under which the pure-jet propulsion engine can be most usefully applied, i.e. at high forward-speeds and at great altitudes". Furthermore the report noted that for a six-cannon fighter of four-hour endurance the high fuel requirements of the gas turbine would give "a very cumbersome aeroplane.... certainly not an efficient fighter" and the two-stroke would be better.

A sleeve of the first compression-ignition V-twin unit. The thirty air ports were .280 inches wide and .955 inches high and were cut on the skew through the wall to promote the swirl that was necessary to get fast enough combustion for a high-speed diesel. This particular sleeve featured two grooves cut into the sealing area to transmit lubricating oil to the upper part of the cylinder.

The initial prospect of very high power, of course, remained an attraction throughout the development, but the discovery that the unit did not suffer from high fuel consumption, the typical defect of the ordinary two-stroke, was a great attraction, particularly after 1940 when the Battle of Britain was over and the threat of invasion had receded, for a large number of different roles and missions for aircraft then became under investigation by military planners for the prosecution of the air war. Many of these clearly seemed to suit the Crecy and a 1943 paper reviewed single- and twin-engined fighters, long-range fighter-bombers, heavy bombers, naval fighters and civil aircraft, concluding that "compared to the Merlin 14SM four-stroke engine the two-stroke gives a small improvement in the top speed, range and take-off distance of almost any aircraft".

Thus the two-stroke was developing its own performance profile, based on studies at the RAE, Rolls-Royce and Ricardo, which was distinct from either the four-stroke or the gas turbine. In May 1944, Ben Lockspeiser, now DSR at the MAP, had a meeting at Derby on the status of two-stroke work, and noted "MAP's keen desire to back up this [exhaust utilisation] development to the maximum possible extent and referred to the advantages of using a two-stroke engine for this purpose and its advantageous position as a link between the piston and jet engines". In effect, this implied that there was likely to be a gap in speed, altitude performance and endurance between the next generation of four-stroke fighters and the coming gas turbine types, which it seemed the two-stroke could fill.

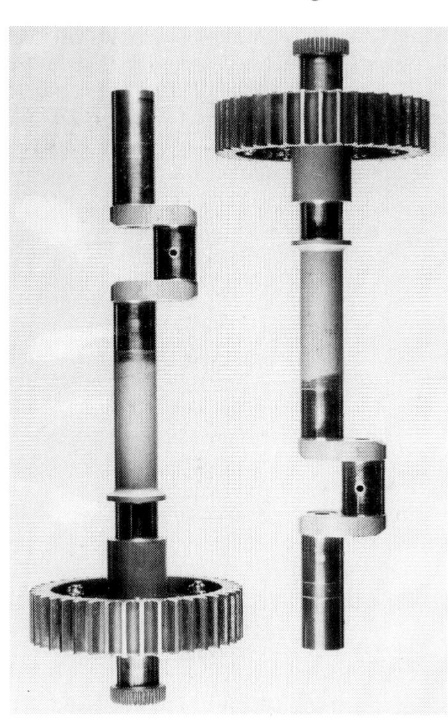

The sleeves of the compression-ignition V-twins were originally driven by cranks and not by eccentrics as in the later builds. This meant that the motion was reciprocal only, without the twist action of the latter.

It is ironical that the two-stroke, conceived initially as a sprint interceptor engine, without regard to fuel consumption, came to be commended, in part, for its economy, but it will be clear that the E.65/Crecy concept used a complex and sophisticated cycle quite unlike that of the basic utilitarian two-stroke with which many people are familiar. The fuel economy also derived from the intended strategy of controlling power by the regulation of fuel injection alone, like the diesel that was the ancestor of the Crecy proposal, avoiding the pumping losses associated with throttling. Dick Foster-Pegg, in the next section, will put his views about throttling the Crecy, which was in fact done, and will show that fuel control alone was not enough to ensure steady running over the whole speed and power range. No doubt a combination of throttling and injection control would have been needed if the engine had reached the flying stage. From the outset it had been found difficult to obtain steady running at idling and low powers and

Ricardo early on (1940) proposed a combination of ignition retard and an alteration of the variable-pitch propellor control law to feather the propellor at low power and provide a braking load. Rolls-Royce also experimented for a while with a valve to spill some of the charge from the cylinder.

Nevertheless, it remains the case that Ricardo, the RAE and designers at Rolls-Royce considered the Crecy, like the diesel and the gas turbine, "a full-throttle engine". In particular, they intended that there would not be any regulation of the airflow at cruising power and that all control in normal flight regimes would be exercised by fuel regulation. For this reason the 'bulb' bell-shaped head was utilised to try and keep a rich mixture near the sparking plug, and although the resulting protruding ridge between the bulb and the main combustion chamber was a bad design feature from the point of view of pre-ignition, since it would retain heat, it was kept throughout the life of the engine. The other unusual strategy was to reverse the functioning of the adapted diesel injection pumps which had a fixed start and a variable end to the injection period so that the start varied and the end point remained fixed. This ensured that at low powers and weak mixtures most of the injection would occur at the end of the scavenge period allowing, it was hoped, a local rich mixture to remain in the bulb. Another Ricardo modification was to eliminate the 'drawback' or 'anti-dribble' valve in the hope that "a little dribble would provide a pocket of rich mixture". This view that virtually all control would be exercised by fuel regulation is typified by a note in a paper from the Two-stroke Engine Division

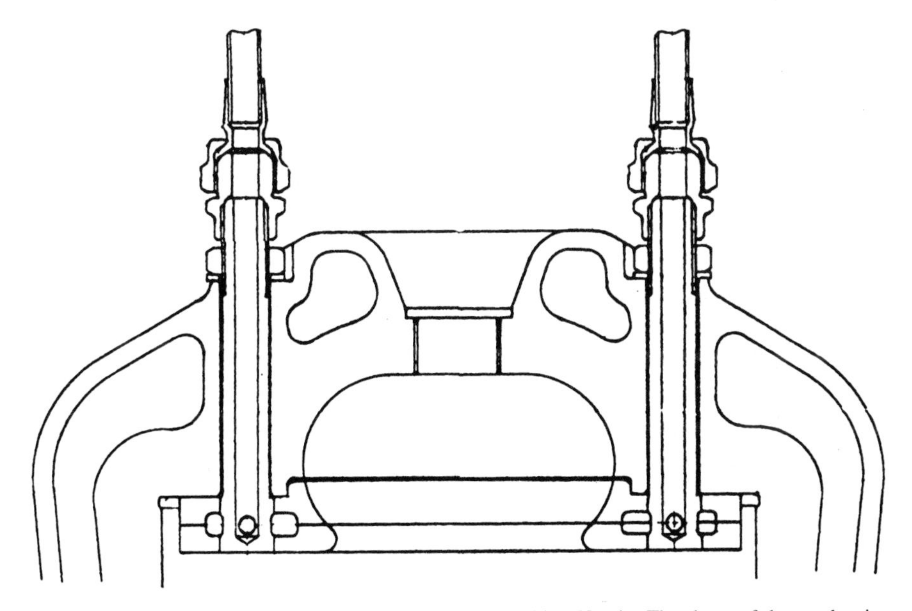

Cross-section through the head of the first compression-ignition V-twin. The shape of the combustion chamber is clear as is the water-cooled hotplate with its lip forming the throat at its base. Also seen are the water-cooling passages through the head.

at Rolls-Royce in December 1944 stating, "the control of power is affected solely by varying the quantity of fuel admitted in the main charge while the quantity admitted to the bulb remains constant at all times".

The development of the fuel injection equipment itself posed considerable problems, as related by George Barton who then worked at CAV in Acton. CAV had built Bosch designs pre-war under licence, but were now cut off from their 'parent' design department and he recalls that they stripped newer captured German injection equipment to test and copy, though they met problems running the pumps on Anglo-American 100-octane fuel for, unlike diesel, petrol has no lubricating qualities. The units finally developed for the Crecy, he believes, incorporated pendulum-type de-aerators that were based on the injection installation of Deckel manufacture from a BMW801 (the Focke-Wulf 190 engine) which was passed to CAV. They were told, for security reasons, that the work was for the Sabre. (As Dick Foster-Pegg relates, there was always plenty of petrol around in Crecy work, and Barton remembers a boy apprentice at CAV passing out from petrol vapour.)

Development of high-speed injection equipment suitable for the two-stroke was certainly one of the hurdles in the Crecy programme and fuel injection may have been partly responsible for the elusive problem of unstable running which was frequently noticed. According to a progress report in 1941 "Rolls-Royce have experienced a considerable amount of unstable running with their twin-cylinder units. At times it has been traced to ignition or injection faults but on other occasions the unit has settled down and run steadily without the cause of the instability being discovered". Even at the end of the war, after four more years of work this problem still occurred, and the RAE in 1946 noted that the Rolls-Royce V-twin unit which they had been using there "with the exception of only two occasions.... never ran really steadily". Interestingly, exhaust thermocouple readings often showed considerable (and variable) differences in temperature between cylinders and even, sometimes, between the two exhaust stubs of the same cylinder. This result might indicate that the problem sometimes originated in an aerodynamic instability in the cylinder charging and scavenge airflow. The unpredictable nature of the performance of the E.65 units is also dwelt on in a 1945 MAP report which commented "it should have been possible for a unit or engine to complete a type-test to any schedule within the framework of the table shown. ....Many lengthy uninterrupted runs at fairly high powers have been made successfully but attempts to repeat them under apparently identical conditions usually failed". As Foster-Pegg will show, development problems existed in many areas and Crecy development was slower than had been hoped.

At a meeting of the ARC in September 1942, Tizard admitted as much with the comment that "he had hoped at one time that [the two-stroke] would take the place of the Merlin. This was not to be, it seemed, since the two-stroke was not ready". It was also noted that the power-to-weight ratios of the two-stroke and the Griffon showed a slight superiority in favour of the Griffon, which would promise a higher rate of climb. Nevertheless, Tizard maintained his faith in the two-stroke, saying that it appeared to him to have "a marked superiority over the Griffon".

The sleeves with which Ricardo had proved the open-ended concept had been of carbon steel (unhardened), running in a cast-iron cylinder and so offered minimal

Sir Harry Ricardo. By the time that he went to Rugby school in 1898 he had owned a screw-cutting lathe since the age of ten, built several steam engines on it, was passionately interested in the internal combustion engine and was already designing and building his own. He became the most esteemed and best-known consultant on internal combustion engine affairs in Britain.

problems in terms of thermal expansion and variation of fits during running. When Ricardo moved to a more flight-worthy alloy cylinder design they chose Lo Ex silicon aluminium alloy of low expansion coefficient. Rolls-Royce, however, designed the cylinder block in stronger RR.50 and therefore adopted an austenitic nitrogen-hardened steel for the sleeve (KE.965) with a higher coefficient of expansion, in order to maintain the sleeve-to-cylinder fit. Bristol sleeve-valve engines used a similar combination of materials but in the two-stroke the sleeve had special problems with hardening and grinding since the narrow bars between ports were prey to becoming overhardened, highly stressed and also caused the grinding wheel to skip, possibly adding mechanical damage. "It is rather unfortunate", commented Ricardo, "that by adopting differences of design and materials, [Rolls-Royce] should have run into troubles from most of which we have been exempt". In part, the problem was that nitrogen-hardening produced a thin skin , and some distortion, so that the hardened surface might be broken through on final grinding to size. There seems, though, little doubt that in the long view Rolls-Royce were best able to judge what materials should be adopted for a practical aero engine. Ricardo's did, in fact, later comment that the Rolls-Royce nitrided KE.965 sleeves were free from wear, "which had been such a tiresome feature of soft carbon sleeves", though they did report a variable effect on ring groove wear. However, later Rolls-Royce sleeves were produced according to the technique developed by the Bristol Aeroplane Co. in which hardened sleeves were 'massaged' to shape by rollers, rather than ground, and then 'satin finished' by a coarse honing process. Ricardo agreed that "these sleeves gave consistent and excellent results with regard to both ring groove and sleeve wear".

By July 1943 the Committee heard from Wood that the problem of wetting the KE.965 sleeve with oil had been solved by machining matching grooves in the pistons and sleeves but "piston cooling was still an unsolved problem. The piston required 35-40 gal/hr/piston, and it had not been possible to get this quantity of oil up the hollow connecting-rods; but the end-to-end system of crankshaft oil supply

It would appear that neither of the two original Crecy engines were properly photographed in their Mk.I state. Fortunately, photographs of the Crecy Mk.I mock-up survive to reveal features that were not evident on the Mk.II. Clearly visible is the one-piece cylinder head and block with the coolant jacket running continuously from the rear to its outlet above the reduction gear housing. The arrangement whereby the coolant from the water pump beneath the engine is fed to the cylinders is not so substantial as with the Mk.II, On that engine the air belt was widened to provide a greater mass flow to the cylinders and the water gallery was included in the same casting. The feed pipes from the injection pump are seen running serpentine-fashion behind the sparking plugs. It is assumed that it was this mock-up that was mated to a Spitfire fuselage at Hucknall to determine installation arrangements.

was being introduced to conserve the amount of oil supplied to the main and eccentric bearings". At this meeting Hooker discussed the relative power of Merlin and Crecy asserting that the latter would be 25-30% more powerful than the former, when both were fitted with the most effective type of ejector exhaust manifolds. As at the other meetings, Spike Corbitt of the Crecy development team took a more optimistic view, looking forward to improvements in valve timings, ports and blower to lift the Crecy advantage. A comparison in September 1944, apparently written by Corbitt, offered the promise of a 50% power advantage for the Crecy and a 15% improvement in consumption at 15,000 feet when fitted to an exhaust turbine, compared with a similarly equipped Merlin. However, his paper also revealed the dispiriting fact that the Crecy had so far been worked up only to 1600 bhp at 2600 rpm compared to 2340 bhp from the current Merlin (at 3000 rpm).

By the end of the war, the two-stroke had revealed itself to be a far more subtle device and to have far more potential than the deceptively simple 'hot-rod' engine concept devised in 1935 to power fighters to counter the threat of aerial bombardment. However, the great progress being made both in performance and efficiency with the gas turbine was making it the clear choice for most military requirements. As the final Rolls-Royce report to the ARC put it (the document is quoted in full in Appendix I) “the Crecy has actually demonstrated the possibility of surpassing the four-stroke in power, consumption at maximum power and heat rejected to coolant. Its principal virtues of furnishing low consumptions at high cruising powers, however, cannot be made use of since the operational requirements for long-range aircraft call for 25-50 percent of maximum take-off power. At this reduced cruising power the four-stroke is actually superior on specific fuel consumption”.

During the war the RAE had made the astute observation that “in any final assessment of the .... Rolls-Royce two-stroke engine it must be remembered that the present rate of development of the two-stroke is much less rapid than that of the four-stroke. The two-stroke’s present margin of improvement may well be bridged by the four-stroke by the time the two-stroke reaches the manufacturing stage”.

A W Morley, one of the engine performance experts concerned with the Crecy studies at the RAE, writing in 1946, gave this view of the project; “The two-stroke has the merit of extreme simplicity and gave early promise of outstanding performance. However, it was never sufficiently far in advance of the comparable Merlin production engines to be worth the risk of far greater effort being spent on it”.

The Aeronautical Research Committee, the ‘godfather of the Crecy’, gave the engine another, more positive, epitaph which some may well agree with today in the light of this account, but which is still open to argument. The words are probably Tizard’s, but the Committee report observed; “Research had revealed that the two-stroke sleeve-valve cylinder was capable of a maximum power output of nearly double that of contemporary four-cycle engines, nearly 200 hp per litre. .... It seems probable that, had the turbine not materialised, the two-stroke would have proved the next step in the development of the aero engine”.

CHAPTER TWO

The PI.26 Crecy R.Cr.1M

by Dick Foster-Pegg P.E.

Rolls-Royce was engaged in the development of the two-cycle engine from 1937 until the programme was abandoned in December of 1945. A separate department was created to design and develop a two-stroke engine. At first it was to be a diesel engine and the department was designated the 'CI' for compression ignition. When the development was changed to petrol it became the 'PI' for petrol injection. The engines were named Crecy only when the first main engine was ordered about 1940. The name derived from the Battle of Crecy, a small Somme town where, on 24 August 1346 the English army defeated the French. All Rolls-Royce two-stroke engines were to be named after battles, though none were to follow the Crecy. The CI/PI/Crecy organisation will be called the Crecy organisation. It was separated

This gloomy photograph taken in the Experimental Shop is the only known picture of the Crecy Mk.I. The tall coolant jackets engulfing the integral cylinder heads can be seen along with the strengthening beams bolted onto them to prevent cracking. This photograph was taken in April 1943, therefore the engine has to be Crecy No.4 as by this time Crecy No.2, the only other to be built as a Mk.I, had been converted to a Mk.II with separate cylinder heads.

The plan view of the mock-up of the Mk.I shows well the original air feed manifold from the supercharger into the cylinders with its two-part construction. The small-bore pipes running along the manifold and into the cylinder blocks supply the oil for upper cylind er sleeve lubrication. Above the pipe ends is the face through which the inner exhaust ports pierce, though none do in this wooden model.

from other Rolls-Royce engine operations, as was normal in Rolls-Royce, and placed under the management of Harry Wood (Wd).

This policy resulted in separate groups for the two-cycle engine within both the drawing and development offices and engine test structures. The first two-cycle engine operated by Rolls-Royce was a single-cylinder Ricardo E.44 diesel with the same bore and stroke as the Kestrel. A petrol-injection single-cylinder test unit based on the E.44, designated the E.65, was also run at Nightingale Road. On the outbreak of war the Company abandoned diesel operation and concentrated on petrol injection. The Crecy engines were liquid-cooled, upright 90-degree vee-12 two-strokes. The angle of the vee was such to allow even-firing at 30 -degree intervals. The cylinders had a single sleeve-valve, petrol injection directly into the combustion chambers and ignition was by spark with charge stratification. The final stage of development included an exhaust-driven turbine. A common drive mechanism operated the sleeves of the two cylinders on each crank. Vee-twins were built rather than single-cylinder engines to allow this sleeve drive mechanism to be tested.

The auxiliaries were driven from the front of the crankshaft to avoid crankshaft torsional vibration. There was a single front-mounted magneto with two independent electrical systems to fire the duplicate sparking-plugs in each cylinder. These features were copied from the Griffon. Each main engine had two six-cylinder, fuel-injection pumps, one mounted at the front of each cylinder block and feeding its cylinders. The blower was located at the rear of the engine and driven by a torsionally flexible shaft running from front to rear. The oil and coolant pumps were also driven by this shaft and the exhaust turbine, when fitted, was geared to it. Eight Crecy vee-twins and six main engines (full twelve-cylinder flight configuration) were built. At least one of the vee-twins was built as a diesel and subsequently converted to petrol injection. Only two turbines were built and fitted briefly to the fourth, fifth and sixth main engines. Main engines were evenly numbered, so the last engine was No.12.

CRECY STATISTICS

General type: Twelve-cylinder, liquid-cooled, upright 90°-vee, two-cycle, sleeve-valve, supercharged.

Details of engine:

Cylinder bore	5.1 in
Piston stroke	6.5 in
Capacity	1536 cu.in (26 litres)
Sleeve stroke	1.950 in
Sleeve thickness	0.120 in
Eccentric phase angle	15° early to crankshaft
Compression ratio	7:1
Propellor reduction ratio	0.451
Supercharger	Centrifugal, single-stage, single-speed
Supercharger rotor dia.	11.7 in
Supercharger eye dia.	7.25 in

Details of engine (cont):

Supercharger gear ratio	8.77 (originally 7.65)
Boost pressure	18 lb/sq.in attained
Direction of rotation	Left-hand tractor
Fuel	100-octane
Sleeve type	Self-sealing, radial ports
Eccentric throw	0.975 in
Sleeve material	KE.965 (later NMC)
Cylinder material	RR.50
Dry weight no turbine	1650 lb
Dry weight with turbine	1800 lb
Dry weight with turbine and contra-rotating reduction gears	1900 lb
Firing intervals	equal 30°
Firing order	A1, B2, A4, B6, A2, B3, A6, B5, A3, B1, A5, B4.

Timings:

Exhaust opens	89° BBDC
Air opens	52° BBDC
Start of fuel injection	BDC at full output
Start of fuel injection	39° after BDC at min output
End of fuel injection	40° ABDC
Exhaust closes	59° ABDC
Air closes	68° ABDC

The crankshaft cranks were spaced 120 degrees apart except cranks 3 and 4 which were 180 degrees apart. The Crecy is placed in perspective if thought of as having approximately the bore of a Kestrel, the stroke of a Griffon and the swept volume of a Merlin.

CRECY RATINGS

Without exhaust turbine

	COMBAT & TAKE-OFF	MAX CLIMB	MAX CRUISE	ECONOMY CRUISE
rpm	2750	2750	2500	2500
Boost psig	15	12	10	10
Altitude ft	0	5000	10000	10000
Propellor hp	1768	1605	1422	1125
Thrust lb	323	315	285	229
Petrol consumption gls/hr			85.4	

With exhaust turbine

	TAKE -OFF	COMBAT CLIMB	MAX CRUISE	MAX CRUISE	ECONOMY
rpm	3000	3000	2750	2750	2750
Boost psig	24	20	15	15	15
Altitude ft	0	10000	10000	10000	10000
Propellor hp	2729	2513	2070	2070	1827
Thrust lb	287	322	238	238	226

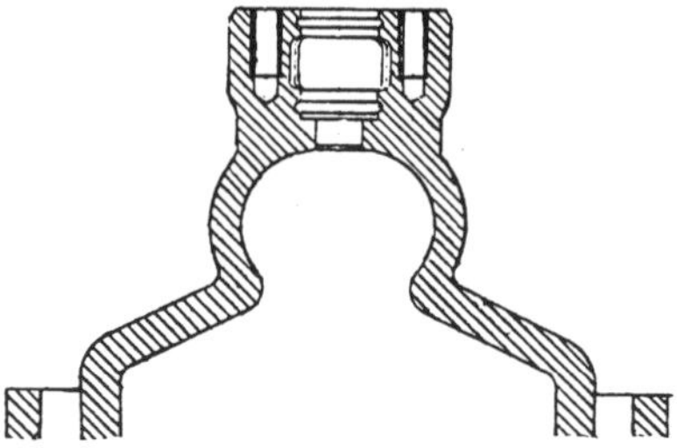

The Crecy Mk.I, like the early Merlin marks, had a one-piece cylinder block/head each with six integral combustion chambers. Shrouding them all was a bolted-on cover within which coolant flowed from one end to the other. This design was nothing but trouble on account of the poor strength of the combustion chamber walls resulting in cracking. A number of strengthening features were evaluated to overcome the problem. The first illustration shows the original design followed by a strengthening of the recess behind the throat of the bulb. Illustration 3 shows an increase in material thickness plus additional strengthening followed by the final scheme which employed a girder arrangement running the length of each head bolted firmly to the cylinder block. This was an expedient to keep the engines running. In all illustrations the water jacket has been omitted for clarity. Interestingly, the final two schemes employed a smaller combustion chamber bulb. A return to the one-piece head was always envisaged as it held the prospect of better fuel economy.

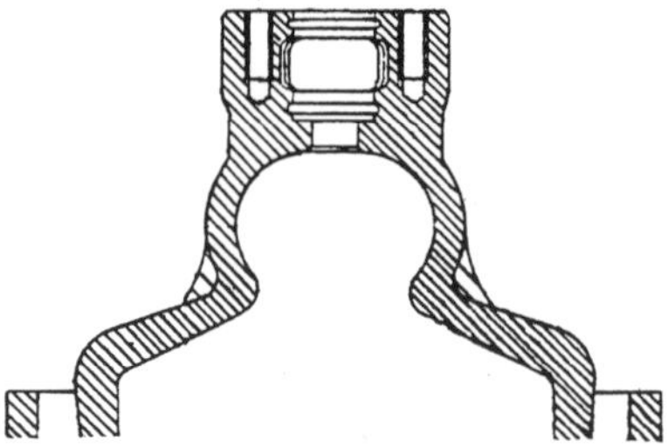

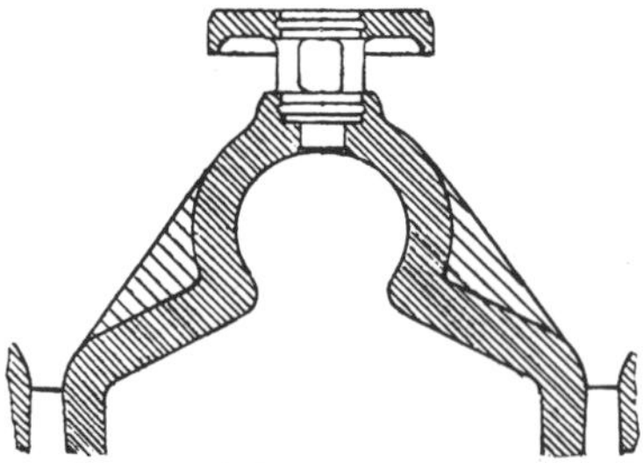

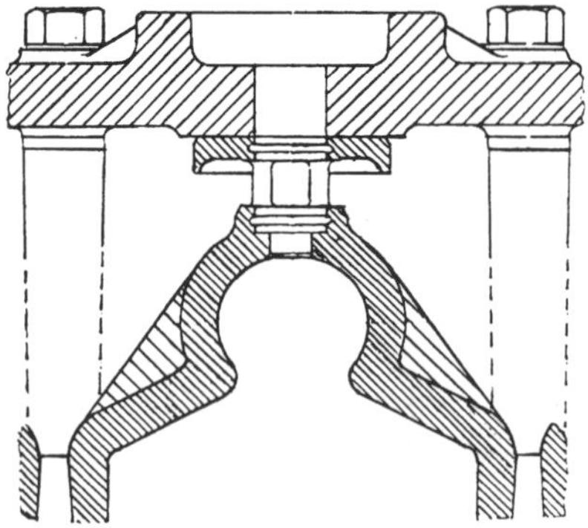

Demonstrated potential

Towards the end of the development the vee-twins were running endurance at 600 crankshaft hp (no blower power deducted). On 21 December 1944 Crecy No.10 attained the highest power measured from a main engine, 1798 bhp and 2350 shp (bhp plus calculated blower power). Corrected for testbed inlet and exhaust pressure losses these powers are about 1850 bhp and 2500 shp. In flight, or with an exhaust turbine, supercharger power would be recovered from the exhaust so crankshaft power is a closer approximation of the engine's potential than brake horse power. Ricardo & Co subsequently ran a Crecy-configuration, single-cylinder engine (E.65) at a power output equivalent to 5000 bhp in a Crecy.

Cylinder blocks and heads

Each of the 6-cylinder blocks was a monobloc casting: on the Mk.I engine the heads were integral, on the Mk.II the heads were separate and each retained by eighteen bolts. Around the top of each cylinder there was an exhaust port encircling its circumference totally, except for four dividing bars whose only purpose were to provide guides for the sleeves to traverse across the gap; and lower down a completely open area forming the air belt. The inside surfaces of the cylinders forming the V were bridged by the air manifold supplying the air from the supercharger. Originally, this was a two-piece design, later replaced by a stronger one-piece casting. In the Mk.I design the water jacket extended from immediately above the air belt to the top of the head, the passages being designed to give the maximum cooling in the region above the exhaust ports and around the combustion chamber.

In the Mk.II the water jacket extended from the air belt to the top of the block only with no internal passage connection to the heads. These were fed from external pipes at the rear of the block, each head was linked in series until the coolant, as per Merlin

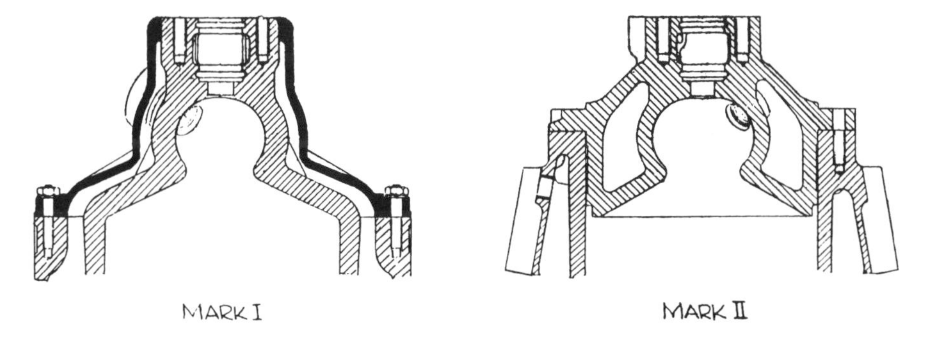

Cross-sections through the two Crecy cylinder head designs. The Mk.I head was an integral casting with the cylinder block (as was the Merlin at that time) and was totally enclosed by a cover within which the coolant flowed. The Mk.II's head was totally different and was detachable with the coolant passages as part of the casting. Note the larger-capacity bulb. The section is cut through the exhaust port dividing bars, thus the ports themselves are not obvious.

practice, exited forward into a header tank.

Just below the exhaust port was a shallow oil groove to supply oil to lubricate the sleeve above the air belt. Near the bottom of the cylinder a contracting ring was fitted to prevent the leakage of boost air into the crankcase.

Combustion chambers

The fuel was injected through a single injector at the centre of each cylinder, spraying into a partial pre-combustion chamber in which the sparking-plugs were located. This arrangement provided a rich mixture around the plugs to initiate a hot flame which would then spread throughout the rest of the cylinder where the mixture was weaker. This was an early stratified charge arrangement. The flame travel from rich to progressively weaker mixture allowed operation without detonation on lower-octane petrol or at higher boost pressures.

Sleeves and sleeve-operating mechanism

The sleeves were open-ended and sealed against the cylinder bore by controlled clearance. The exhaust discharged from the cylinders over the top of the sleeves around the full 360 degrees of the circumference and through ports each side of the cylinder block, creating as free an area as is conceivable. This arrangement was a Ricardo invention and is unique to the Ricardo single-cylinder engines and the Crecy. The sleeve expanded as it heated, reducing the oil film, until the heat transferred through the oil film to the cylinder wall equalled the heating of the sleeve by the combustion giving a self-adjusting fit.

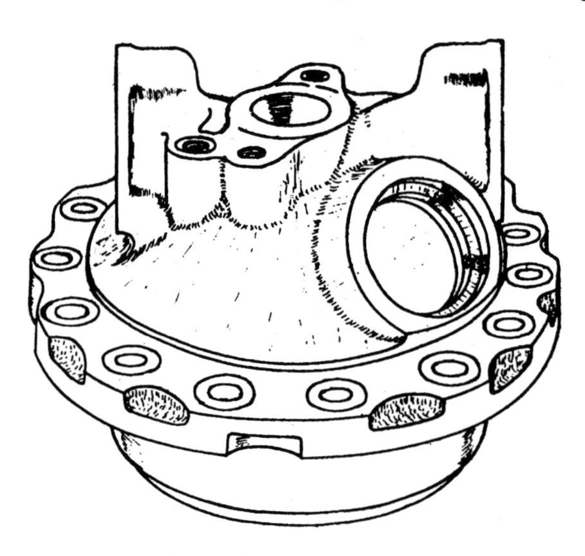

The Crecy Mk.II's separate cylinder head. The large orifice (another on opposite side) takes the water-cooled sparking-plug adaptor, and the centre hole the fuel injector. The latter is flanked by the coolant inlet and outlet connections.

The sleeve motion controlled the opening and closing of the exhaust ports while the inlet air ports machined in the sleeves were opened and closed by the piston. The sleeve-valves of four-stroke engines reciprocate at half crankshaft speed driven by small gear-driven cranks. In the two-cycle Crecy everything happened each revolution and the sleeves reciprocated in phase with the crankshaft. This

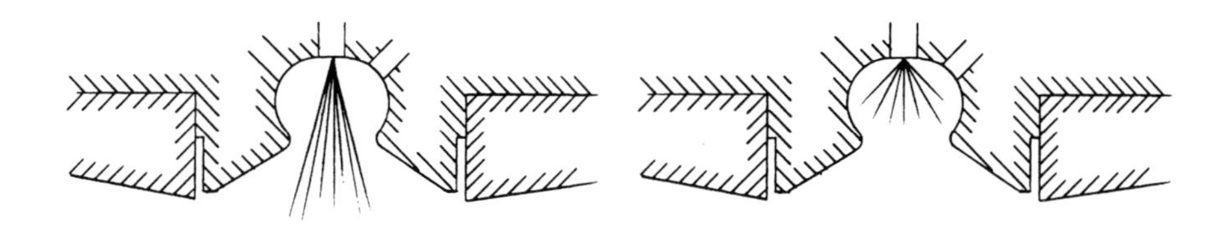

The stratification of the mixture was not achieved simply by the shape of the head, it was also necessary to adjust the pattern of the injection spray. The injection apparatus was modified CAV-Bosch equipment. With diesel operation it is the practice to give a sharp cut-off to the injection period, but for the Crecy the pump 'drawback' valves were modified to give a slower pressure decay in the pipes at the end of the injection period, and thus a coarse, dribbling spray into the bulb. This combination of injection pattern and combustion chamber profile would allow the speed to be controlled, it was hoped, on petrol regulation alone. Ricardo found that the engine would idle with perfect regularity and run up to about 15% of full torque with combustion taking place in the bulb alone. From there on to 40% of full torque combustion was irregular and uncertain. Above that figure, smooth running returned.

allowed a most elegant sleeve drive mechanism operated by eccentrics integral with the crankshaft webs, a system beautiful in its simplicity and which gave few problems. The sleeves were reciprocated by a large diameter strap around the eccentric lined with a lead-bronze bearing. The eccentric straps were prevented from rotating by guide pistons on the engine centreline. Each eccentric drove two sleeves by pins and ball joints imparting an eliptical motion to the sleeve which distributed oil between sleeve and cylinder. The continuous motion between piston and sleeve was claimed to reduce ring and sleeve wear at the top of the stroke.

It is ironic that the only available photograph of a sleeve drive mechanism shows a failure. This occurred on the first vee-twin when it was operating as a diesel and is the only failure of this part of the eccentric sleeve drive which the author can remember.

The top edge of a sleeve was open to cylinder pressure, there being no junkhead to seal the gas pressure as in four-cycle, sleeve-valve engines. The sleeves were about an eighth of an inch thick and the area of the end of a sleeve was one tenth of the area of a piston. The sleeve stroke was about a third of the piston stroke so the gas pressure on a sleeve contributed about 3% of the work of a piston. Because the sleeve led the piston by 15 degrees the contribution of the sleeves to the engine power was usually quoted as being 2%. The flow of power between sleeve and crankshaft reversed during the cycle. The eccentric drive was better able to handle this reversal than a geared crankshaft with its inevitable backlash. The orbital sleeve motion of the eccentric drive was better for lubrication and the whole scheme was more direct and simple, thus justifying its selection.

The sleeves of four-cycle engines were lubricated by splash from the crankcase, but in the Crecy the top outsides of the sleeves were isolated from the crankcase by the air inlet belt, which fed the inlet ports in the sleeve, and thus required a separate oil supply. The oil was provided by a pump which metered a small quantity of oil to each sleeve outer surface. Because the air belt around the cylinder prevented blow-by, or carbon from burned fuel, from reaching the crankcase, the oil remained clear and golden at all times, like in a jet engine. In four-cycle piston engines the oil quickly turns black as ink.

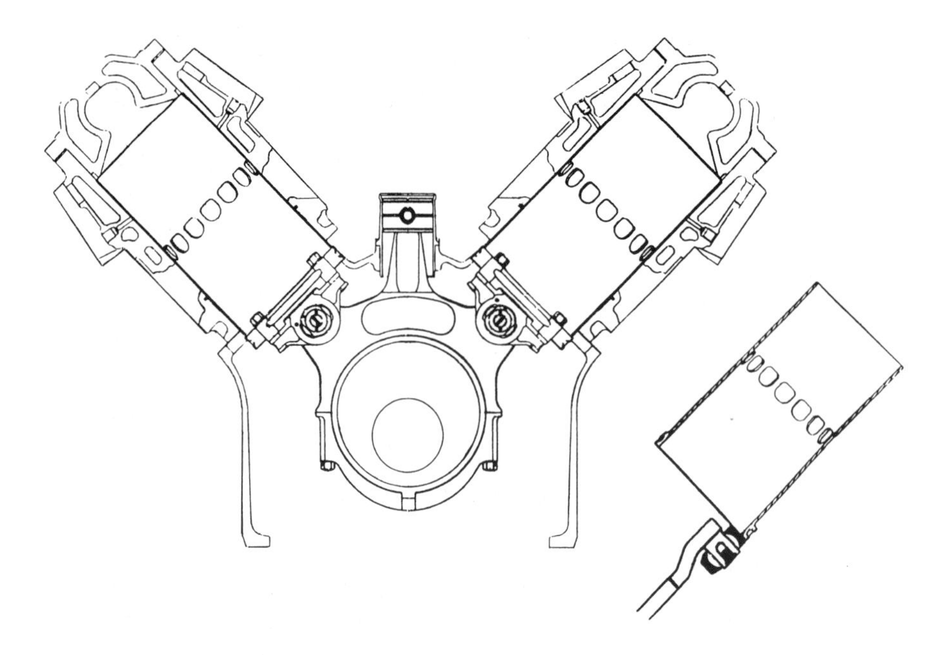

The Crecy sleeves and their drive mechanism. Both sleeves are attached to the eccentric bearing (strap) by spherical ball-joints; the small open-topped piston in the centre ensuring that the position of the whole assembly cannot be disturbed by the rotation of the crankshaft eccentric that drives it. In this cross-sectional view the slice is taken through two of the opposed vertical bars (four in all) that equally divide the circumference of the 360° exhaust port, hence the port does not appear on the drawing. The position of the eccentric web on the crankshaft gives the reader an understanding of how its offset centre produces the 1.950-inch travel of the sleeves and how the small amount of movement to left and right during the travel produces an eliptical motion. This ensured that, unlike linear motion, the sleeve never actually came to a stop at TDC or BDC.

Oil-cooled pistons

The pistons of two-cycle engines are exposed to hot combustion gas for a greater proportion of time than four-stroke pistons and it is common practice to augment transfer of heat from the pistons to the cylinder walls with cooling by oil. In the case of the Crecy, and all sleeve-valved engines, the sleeve creates an extra barrier to heat flow between the piston and the coolant. Oil cooling was accomplished by oil fed from the crankshaft through drillings in the connecting-rods. The piston cooling oil either sprayed onto the underside of the crown of a one-piece piston or was fed into a space inside a two-piece piston where it was directed to the edges via radial grooves. (A two-piece, oil-cooled piston frequently used in diesel engines is called a 'cocktail shaker'.) The two systems of piston cooling seemed to work equally well. The pistons of the Pennine engine were cooled by static oil-jets directed up from the crankcase wall and this system was under consideration for the Crecy. Oil cooling of

The interim Crecy Mk.II engine, easily distinguishable as such by the Mk.I's rearward-sloping magneto assembly and the Mk II's separate cylinder heads. The extremely wide looking cylinder block is evident with its combined air belt/coolant feed gallery. Air from the manifold positioned within the V of the cylinder blocks entered an airbelt that completely surrounded the cylinders and entered them via a port encircling its full circumference. The forward face of the block is taken up by the injection pumps, the pipes from each travelling rearward to each injector in the centre of each cylinder head. Fuel is fed to the injection pumps via the de-aerator/ filter (later deleted) assembly on front left of engine. It is almost certain that this is Crecy No.2, the prototype engine.

It is ironic that the only photograph available of the Crecy's sleeve and sleeve-drive mechanism depicts a rare failure of the latter experienced on the original compression-ignition V-twin engine. The circular strap was clamped around one arm of each crankshaft web and was, of course, slightly eccentric to the crankshaft to give the up and down movement to the sleeves. This engine's original configuration featured sleeves driven by small crankshafts giving only straight up and down motion. These were replaced by the above scheme which gave a rotating motion during the sleeve's rise and descent thus assisting lubrication by wiping the oil between sleeve and cylinder walls. During each revolution the path of the drive arm would describe an elipse. The small piston between the sleeves acts as a guide to prevent rotation of the strap. Having no crown it is open-topped and runs within the small cylinder seen lying adjacent to the power piston. The two circular plates on the left are the hot plates bolted into the combustion chamber to assist compression ignition.

the Merlin's pistons was also being considered at the end of its development.

With the reciprocating motion the oil in the drilling through the length of the connecting-rods was propelled towards the piston as the rod slowed on the up-stroke and accelerated on the down-stroke. The oil was propelled away from the pistons as the rod decelerated and accelerated at the bottom of the stroke. To prevent the oil from returning towards the crank at the bottom of the stroke the grooves in the con-rod big-end bearing were arranged to connect with the drilling in the crankshaft only when the inertial forces were acting to push the oil towards the piston. Feeding of oil into the ends of the crankshaft as well as through the main bearings was incorporated in the Crecy towards the end of development at the insistence of Hives.

Ring groove wear was an early problem and was solved by circular steel inserts cast into the pistons in which the grooves were machined. This is common practice in diesels.

Two examples of piston failure as suffered by V-twin No.7. That on the left shows the result of pre-ignition which in turn created enough heat to cause the alloy cylinder to pick-up on the sleeve. The other shows damage caused by ring breakage. These are two-piece pistons, the connecting bolts of which can be seen on the crowns. The dark band around the lower half is recessed to carry oil above the air ports in the cylinder wall. The right-hand piston also has an oil-retaining groove below the bottom compression ring.

The two-piece, oil-cooled piston. Opposite-end views of each part are shown. Plainly seen are the twenty grooves radiating from the centre to the edge and the recesses forming the two wells into which the oil collected.

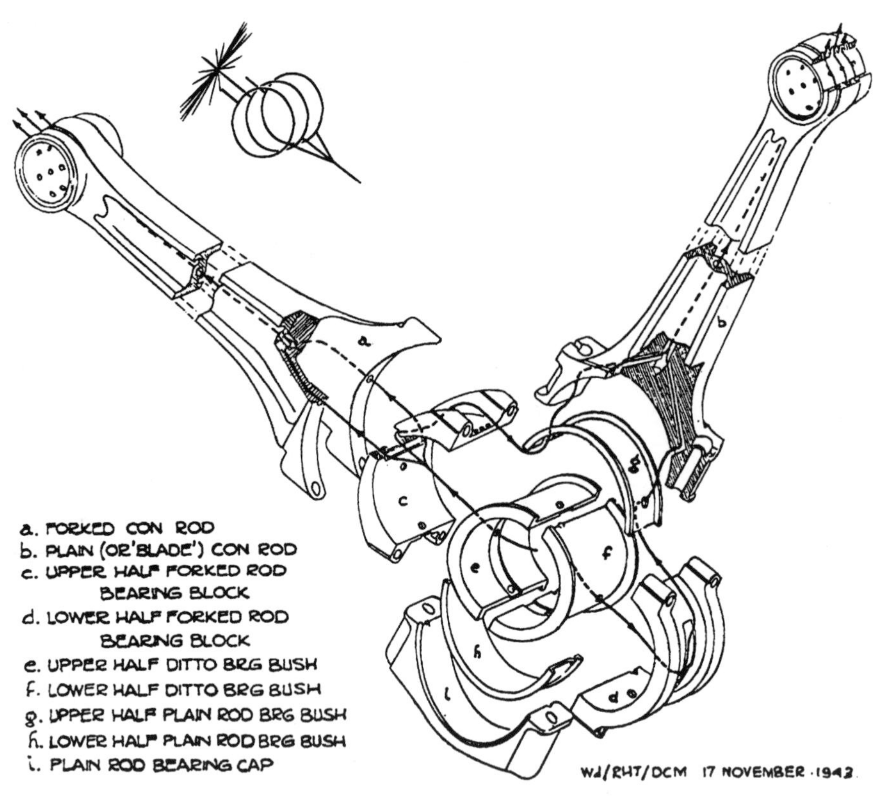

The method of supplying cooling oil to the pistons involved, in later designs, a timing sequence whereby oil from within the crankshaft fed into radially-cut grooves in the rod bearing bushes over an arc of 150 degrees (80 and 120-degree arcs were also evaluated) so that the hole in the bottom of both con-rods (blade and fork) were fed with oil for the duration of their travel over the arc, the angle of which best exploited the upward inertia effect. Because the oil in the Crecy always remained clean and pure there was no problem of sludge silting-up the holes and grooves. The scrap view shows the route the oil takes, via three passages, around the con-rod little-end.

Power control

In reports about two-cycle engines the statement will be found "a two-cycle engine can not be throttled". This statement causes a lot of confusion because it is misunderstood. The Crecy was fitted with throttles just like the Merlin, Griffon, etc. The throttles controlled the airflow into the engine just as in the four-cycle engines. In the often-quoted confusing statement 'throttling' means the reduction of the inlet manifold pressure below the atmospheric exhaust pressure as occurs in four-cycle engines.

In a four-cycle engine petrol/air mixture is drawn into the cylinder by the piston.

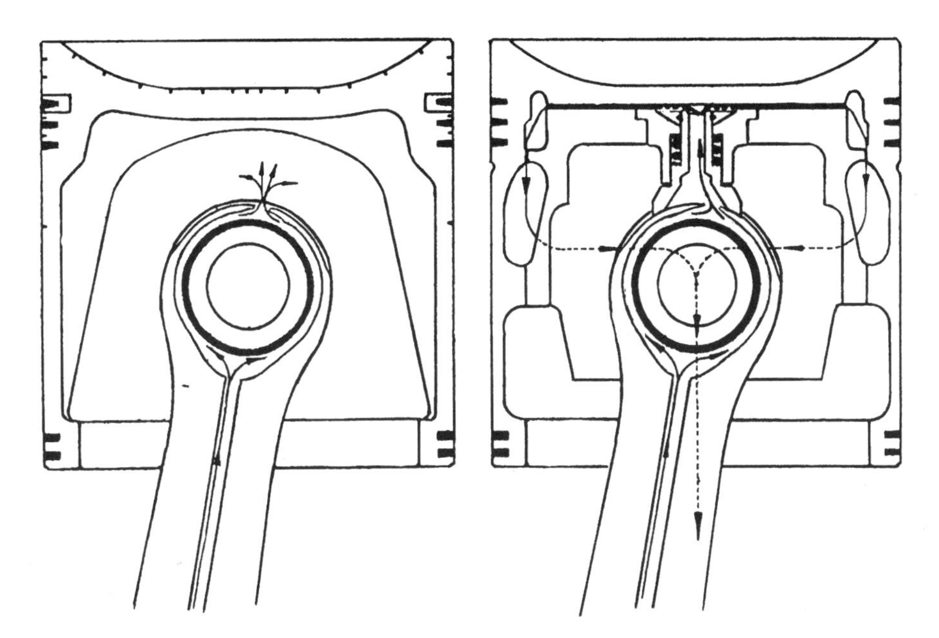

Cross-sections through the one-piece and two-piece pistons showing the oil flow paths. Oil was pumped up from the crankshaft via drillings in the con-rods to flow around the little-end bush in three streams (originally only one) and out through holes in its top. The rocking motion of the con-rod sprayed the oil over the underside of the piston after which it ran down the sides of the piston and into the sump. For the two-piece piston the oil from the centre stream only was directed via a collector to exit in the centre of the inner piston and travel outwards along radial grooves taking with it the heat from the crown of the outer piston. It then over-ran the edge to fall into a well behind the piston rings, through holes into a larger well from which it exited around the gudgeon-pin holes to fall into the sump. Tests showed that the two-piece piston ran about 100°C cooler on its non-thrust side. Flow rate was a round 50 gph at 2750 rpm. The one-piece piston shows the fusible plugs, 1/16-inch diameter, 1/8-inch deep, inserted into the crown and lands. This sentinel method of assessing piston temperatures employed wire of eutectic composition, various metals being used to obtain the required melting points. The plugs were placed in groups of four so as to cover the range of temperatures likely to be found at a particular part of the piston. The coolest parts, below the compression ring, were recorded at around 150°C; and the hottest , on the crown and on the rim on the non-thrust side at 400°C. This was with the one-piece piston, the two-piece piston peaking at 340°C. Note the cast-in steel insert retaining the upper compression ring. This was to prevent the serious wear that occurred to the land due to insufficient lubrication. Note also that all compression rings were of taper section.

If naturally aspirated the engine operates at full power if un-throttled. To provide a lower power, the pressure in the inlet manifold is throttled to below atmospheric pressure. This reduces the flow of mixture commensurate with the required power, even near zero for engine idle. In the four-cycle engines the throttles controlling airflow are the primary control of power, as in cars. The fuel is controlled automatically by the carburettor or injection pump providing a single-lever control of power.

In a two-cycle engine there is zero flow through the cylinder and therefore zero power if the inlet manifold pressure is the same as the exhaust pressure. Engine idle is achieved with an inlet manifold pressure of a pound or two per square inch above the exhaust manifold pressure whereas in a four-cycle idle occurs at minus 10 psig. At zero psig manifold pressure the Meteor tank engine, an unsupercharged Merlin, produced about 500 bhp. At the same inlet manifold pressure the Crecy would produce no power. (The normal two-cycle petrol engine used in motorcycles and chain saws etc. uses crankcase compression so it pumps air like a four-cycle and is throttled to a minus pressure at inlet to the crankcase for low-power operation).

All Crecy engines were fitted with inlet throttles like the Merlin, Griffon, etc. Airflow control, by means of the blower throttle, was its primary power control. Because it operated over a range of power from about 60 percent to full power with constant air flow the air throttle was less significant than in four-cycle engines which operated over a narrow range of air/fuel.

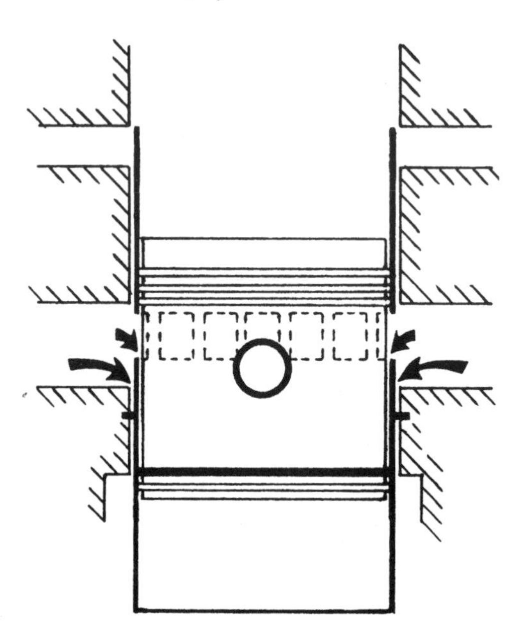

During the compression period the air from the supercharger was prevented from entering the sleeve by the latter covering the inlet port in the cylinder. To prevent it blowing down the clearance between the two and into the crankcase, a sealing ring encircled the sleeve below the port. Similarly, when the sleeve ports lined up with the entry port in the cylinder a boost sealing ring around the piston skirt, above the oil scraper, prevented air from taking this alternative route to the crankcase. With the piston at the top of its stroke, the sealing ring remained below the air ports in the sleeve, thus maintaining freedom from crankcase pressurisation. For this reason Crecy pistons were longer than those employed in four-stroke engines. The clearances shown here are exaggerated for clarity.

The Crecy had not reached the sophistication of a single-lever control and the tester manually controlled RPM and power by the blower throttle, which controlled the airflow, and the rack of the injection pump which regulated fuel flow. The throttle and fuel rack were controlled by a system of rods and cranks from the control position. Ultimately a single-lever control would have been developed for the Crecy before it could have been flown.

The stratified charge combustion chamber in the Ricardo and Crecy engines extended the operable range of air/fuel ratio from about 15 to 23, covering a power range of 100 to 60% at a given airflow and boost pressure. If the air/fuel ratio was increased beyond about 23 the engine misfired, compared to a four-cycle which would cut out at about 14 ratio. The belief that the Crecy could be operated from idle to full load without modulating the airflow is a fallacy.

Airflow system

During all the development a single-stage, single-speed supercharger was fitted with a vortex throttle to improve efficiency when throttled. As stated, a two-stroke engine will not operate unless the inlet manifold pressure exceeds the exhaust pressure to drive out the exhaust products and introduce fresh air into the cylinder. The blower was the only means of filling and emptying the cylinders of the Crecy. Air flowed from the blower through a trunk pipe in the valley of the vee between the cylinders; an air belt extended around and between the cylinders so air could enter them through ports pierced all around the sleeves. Ports for the air to enter the cylinder were opened and closed by the piston at the bottom of its stroke. With the fresh charge of air entering at the bottom of the cylinder and the exhaust discharging at the top, there was end-to-end scavenging which is recognised as important for efficient operation of two-cycle engines. The fresh charge of air was typically 1.5 times the swept volume of the cylinder which, coupled with the end-to-end scavenging, ensured a clean charge of air for each cycle.

Ignition system

The Crecy had two parallel ignition systems each feeding one of the two independent sparking plugs in each cylinder, so the engine could continue to operate if one system failed, as in all other spark-ignition aircraft engines. The two electrical systems were contained in a single magneto similar to the Griffon units designed to run at half speed or about 1200 rpm. On the Crecy they operated at 3000 rpm and did not last very long at the higher speed. The weakest link was the contact-breaker system fitted with stronger return springs to operate at the higher speed. The cam followers and electrical contact points suffered rapid wear and the return springs failed in fatigue after about 50 hours of operation.

At the end of the development the magnetos were still fitted with 'Heath-Robinson' rubber pads to back up the breaker springs and help keep them operating. The high rate of sparking would be no problem for a modern electronic ignition system.

The magnetos on the first series of main engines were mounted at an angle and on subsequent engines were mounted vertically. The sparking-plugs in the Crecy gave almost no trouble.

Fuel-injection system

At maximum power the Crecy rotated at 3000 rpm, and being a two-stroke the fuel-injection pumps also rotated at 3000 rpm. They were basically diesel pumps manufactured by CAV and modified for the Crecy. The design was derived from the German Bosch diesel pumps for four-cycle engines which operated at half engine speed. Like the magnetos the pumps had to operate at more than twice their design speed. The CAV pumps used camshafts and return springs. They were generally reliable but the rate of injection was slower than optimum.

A petrol-injection pump was under development by Rolls-Royce. It was similar

Two examples of sparking-plug lead-fouling experienced on one of the V-twin engines. Lead deposits formed on the electrodes during prolonged running at cruising powers, the remedy being to open up to high boost for a period to clear them. The Crecy was no different from any other engine in this respect where fuel with a high lead content was employed.

in operating principle to the CAV pumps except that a miniature crankshaft and connecting rods were used to operate the plungers. A two-cylinder pump was built and ran on a vee-twin. The Rolls-Royce pump could accommodate larger-diameter elements and thus was capable of injecting more fuel in fewer degrees of crankshaft rotation, important for higher outputs.

Standard industrial diesel engine injectors were used. They were massive steel units and incongruous for an engine designed to fly. The twelve injectors must have added several pounds to the total weight of an engine. Lighter and more compact designs are now available for automotive applications.

Fractures of the fuel-injection pipes between the pumps and the cylinder injectors occurred frequently (typically, one of the twelve pipes might fail each ten-hours of operation), this resulting in petrol at high pressure being sprayed over the hot engine. The blast of air blowing over the engines on the test stands prevented fires but the result inside an aircraft cowling would be unthinkable.

These failures were attributed to the extremely rapid rise in pressure and the twice-normal frequency of injection compared to four-cycle diesel operation. This was a problem with the German four-cycle engines which used direct fuel-injection. Each pressure pulse felt to the touch as though the pipe had been hit with a hammer. Initially the injectors of the main engines were connected to the pumps by the shortest pipes possible, the pipe to No.1 cylinder being the shortest and to No.6 cylinder being the longest. Latterly, the pipes were all made the same length as that to No.6 cylinder to eliminate the small differences in injection speeds. When the first equal-length pipes were to be tested instructions were to coil the extra length of pipes at the injector end. The author decided to make the coils at the pump end and so it remained on all future engines. All pipes were cut to the length of the pipe to No.6 cylinder which had no coil. The pipe to No.5 had one coil and No.4 had two, etc. The injection pipes fitted to the twin units were made the same length as those of the main engines.

The injection of fuel at full delivery started almost 60° before the exhaust closed. Although several degrees of crank motion occurred before the spray penetrated through the combustion zone some fuel was lost into the exhaust. This was with the CAV pump with 10 mm plungers. The Rolls-Royce injection pump with larger plungers would have shortened the injection period and allowed it to be started later.

Exhaust system and turbine

There were two exhaust manifolds to each bank of cylinders, making four in all. With a well-designed exhaust system power expended in driving a supercharger is recovered in flight as exhaust thrust. A Merlin obtains about 150 lb of thrust from its exhaust. The Crecy being a two-stroke passed twice as much air as the Merlin and the blower power and exhaust energy were commensurately higher. The Crecy was expected to obtain 350 lb exhaust thrust at first-flight rating without a turbine. At 300 mph one pound thrust is equal to about one hp into an 80% efficient propeller.

With an exhaust turbine and at the more advanced combat rating, blower power was expected to be about 750 hp, turbine power 800 hp and exhaust thrust 300 lb for about 2500 hp into the propellor plus 300 lb thrust. The turbine was a one-half scale of the turbine of the first Whittle-type jet designed and built by Rolls-Royce, the WR1. With a turbine the four exhaust manifolds were connected into a volute feeding the turbine which was geared into the train connecting the crankshaft and the supercharger. The turbine exhausted through a nozzle and jet thrust remained substantial. The Crecy was tested with the flight-configuration turbine exhaust collector which had two outlets to feed nozzles each side of the engine nacelle, though on the testbed they discharged into the two exhaust stacks.

Turbines were not available until 1945 and little running was accomplished with them as teething problems were encountered. In one episode the engine was running rough and a turbine gear failed allowing the turbine to overspeed. The overspeed stretched the roots of the blades which then rubbed the casing heating it to a cherry red. Blade machining capacity was limited and several months passed before a replacement set of blades was available. If the emphasis was on power for take-off, or on low cruising fuel consumption, an exhaust turbine was a better solution than ejector exhaust nozzles.

The Crecy exhaust port opened almost instantly, not like a poppet valve which opens gradually, and it opened at 91 degrees after top dead centre when the pressure in the cylinder was still high. The exhaust pulses were very strong and the exhaust decibel level was high as a result. In full cry at 3000 rpm there were 36,000 pulses per minute, twice the frequency of other Rolls-Royce engines. (Two cylinders fired and exhausted together in the Rolls-Royce 24-cylinder, four-cycle engines so they sounded like 12-cylinder engines). The combination of the rapid opening and high pressure of the exhaust and the high frequency of the pulses produced an exhaust noise like no other. This is the most remembered feature of the Crecy, indeed it is said that when the engine first ran, the air-raid sirens went off in Nottingham, fifteen miles away! Screamers were attached to the Junkers Ju87 Stuka dive bomber to scare the hell out of the recipients of its load. There would have been no need to add anything to a Crecy-engined plane.

The beautifully compact turbo-blower installation. The single-outlet exhaust was for calibration tests, the definitive design being bifurcated. The turbine was scaled down from the WR-1 gas turbine engine and was driven by the influx from the four exhaust manifolds. On the face of the updraught intake to the supercharger can be seen the two spindles that operate the vortex throttles that give the air pre-swirl as it enters the eye of the blower.

The exhaust turbine showing three of the four gas feed inlets. Note the De Laval bulb roots of the turbine blades as employed on the early gas turbine engines.

Supercharger

A supercharger with a rotor diameter of 11.7 inches was used for most of the main engine operation. Mechanically the Crecy blower gave no problems though its drive by a flexible shaft from the front of the engine was nothing but trouble until a freewheel was inserted in the drive. The rotating guide vanes (RGV) of the blower were 7.25-inch in diameter and were formed by conical turning. They were later used successfully in the Derwent V and Nene jet engines. Unlike the four-cycle engines, the Crecy blower had to supply air to scavenge the burnt gases as well as to compress and burn. It has to be remembered also, that it only compressed air and not an air/fuel mixture.

Airflow through the engine was increased to try to improve the cooling of the pistons by increasing the port areas. The different port areas changed the engine swallowing capacity and the matching of the blower flow to the engine flow. This all complicated and added to the work of Geoff Wilde's supercharger department.

The Crecy blowers were all designed for full-throttle operation at sea level. A blower designed for power at altitude, where the air is of a lower density, operates

The Crecy mock-up engine with exhaust-driven turbo-blower fitted. This particular design featured bifurcated outlets to suit aircraft installation whereby the efflux was expelled either side of a nacelle or fuselage. The connection into the supercharger drive gearing can be clearly seen. This energy could, by redesign, be used to supplement the drive to the propellor by having the exhaust energy drive a turbine geared into the reduction gear, though this particular scheme was not envisaged for the Crecy. Note also that the injector feed pipes are coiled adjacent to the injector instead of at the pump.

One of the very few surviving pieces from the Crecy programme is Spike Corbitt's conically-turned rotating guide vanes. The vanes ensured that the incoming air was most efficiently directed on to the supercharger rotor. It is thought that this particular example is a development piece as those fitted to the supercharger rotors had flat trailing-edges to blend with the rotor vane profiles, as c an be seen in the cut-away drawing.

part-throttled at sea level and physically is much larger than one designed for full-throttle at sea level. The blowers fitted to other engines were all designed for full-throttle only at altitude. This distorts any comparison of size with Crecy blowers. The Crecy was a 26-litre two-cycle which means it passed approximately as much air as a 60-litre four-cycle and needed a large blower.

Various schemes were evaluated and tested on the supercharger rig to increase the capacity of the blowers. A large intake elbow with a larger radius into the eye was tried but the vortex effect was reduced diminishing the swirl. An axial entry was also evaluated which gave an excellent 83% efficiency but would have complicated installation in an aircraft. An 8.25-inch diameter intake eye was tried, hopefully to provide intake swirl at full throttle and a 40% increase in capacity.

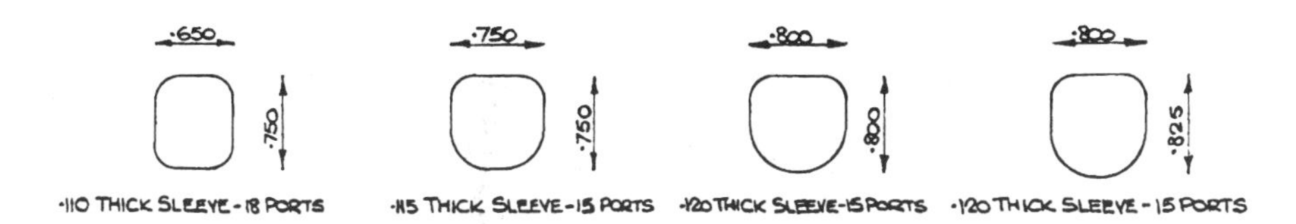

With the objective of improving the strength of the sleeves at the air port belt whilst at the same time trying to pass as much air as possible through them, the ports were gradually reduced in number and increased in area. The ports were cut squarely through the wall of the sleeve and not on the skew as had been those in the compression-ignition V-twin sleeves with the object of promoting swirl.

Taking a leaf out of the R engine's book, a double-entry supercharger was designed and rig-tested but results were disappointing. Rotor diameters of 8.25- and 9.75-inches were tried. It was found that the limited space available on a main engine restricted the air flow into either side. This same problem caused the double-sided blower of the Napier Sabre to be dropped in favour of a single-sided unit.

None of these modifications offered any worthwhile improvement before all test work ceased. However, it should be stated that the Crecy blowers used on the engines were equally efficient as those on other engines of the period.

Engine timings and settings

Optimum inlet port timing is when the ports open and close at the crank positions when the pressures in the cylinder are equal to the boost pressure. The optimum time for the exhaust ports to open is the latest which will allow the exhaust gas to escape and the pressure in the cylinder to fall to boost pressure by the time the inlet ports are open for the fresh charge. The exhaust stays open to allow the fresh charge to sweep the cylinder clean and closes while the inlets are still open to trap air in the cylinder for the pressure to rise to equal the boost. The optimum timings cannot be calculated and are established by trial and error based on dynamometer performance and the comparison of many tests.

Optimum timings were primarily established on the Ricardo single-cylinder engines in which the sleeves were driven by cranks, shafts and gears. This allowed the timimg of the sleeve relative to the crankshaft to be changed by typical vernier splines. The first Rolls-Royce vee-twin two-cycle engine also had gear- and crank-operated sleeves on which the sleeve relationship relative to the crankshaft could be changed. This engine was later modified to eccentric-sleeve operation and all subsequent twins and main engines were built with eccentrics.

The duration of the opening of the exhaust could be changed by machining the top of the sleeves or the ports in the cylinder blocks, and of the inlets by machining the ports in the sleeve or the top edge of the pistons. No change could be made without machining or changing sleeves.

The timing of the Crecy port openings relative to the piston motion was determined by the orientation of the sleeve-driving eccentrics relative to the cranks, both integral with the crankshaft. Once set the timing could not be changed without a new crankshaft. The normal timing was for the eccentrics to lead the cranks by

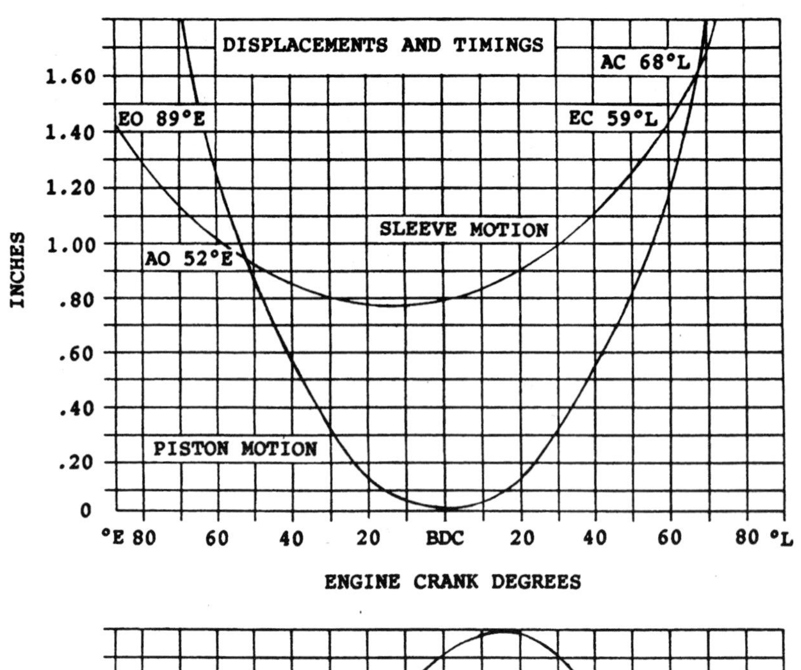
DISPLACEMENTS AND TIMINGS
AC 68°L
EO 89°E
EC 59°L
SLEEVE MOTION
AO 52°E
PISTON MOTION
INCHES
1.60
1.40
1.20
1.00
.80
.60
.40
.20
0
°E 80
60
40
20
BDC
20
40
60
80 °L
ENGINE CRANK DEGREES

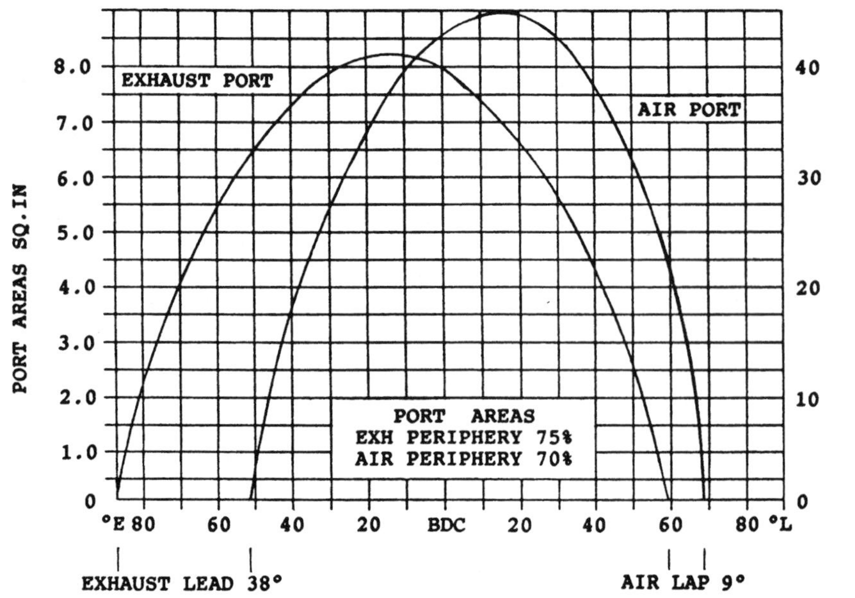
EXHAUST PORT
AIR PORT
PORT AREAS
EXH PERIPHERY 75%
AIR PERIPHERY 70%
PORT AREAS SQ.IN
8.0
7.0
6.0
5.0
4.0
3.0
2.0
1.0
0
°E 80
60
40
20
BDC
20
40
60
80 °L
40
30
20
10
0
EXHAUST LEAD 38°
AIR LAP 9°

AREAS AS A PERCENTAGE OF PISTON AREA

fifteen degrees. The fuel-injection and spark-ignition timings could be changed by vernier adjustments of the spline drives as in four-cycle engines.

The optimum timing of four-cycle engines includes valve lead, lag and overlap, like the Crecy but not to the same extent. The power of all engines is reduced by the period that the valves are open during the working strokes. This effect is greater for two-cycles than for four, but then the two-cycle does not waste half of its revolutions emptying and filling the cylinders. On the four-cycle engines the duration of opening and overlap requires a new camshaft, or new sleeves, but timing of the valve openings relative to the crankshaft can be adjusted by vernier setting of the spline drives. Ignition timing was variable with maximum advance ten degrees before top dead centre.

Mk.II differences

The first two engines, Nos.2 and 4, both ran initially as Mk.Is. Crecy No.6 and the three subsequent engines were all built as Mk.IIs.

Externally, the most obvious change was the vertical positioning of the magnetos from their previous 45° angle behind the top of the propellor reduction gear. The exhaust ports now protruded from the cylinder block to allow the fitment of a flexible manifold. The cylinder heads were detachable and did not form part of the head casting. The original air manifold lying between the cylinder banks was a two-piece affair, the centre part, at which the two halves were joined, was necked down resulting in a restriction of the air supply to the forward cylinders. On the Mk.II the manifold was enlarged to a one-piece assembly without the restriction and to enable better distribution through the cylinder inlet, which was now receiving more air, the air belt was widened on the outer sides of the block. This was achieved by the enlargement of the cast gallery running down the sides of the blocks which also contained an internal passage to carry coolant from the pump to the cylinders. Other minor differences included the re-siting of the constant speed unit and tachometer drive. Coiled fuel injector feed pipes were used for the first time, each being 46 inches in length.

Internally, the shape of the combustion chambers was changed slightly to give a larger-diameter bulb with a smaller-angle cone. The sleeves were .2 inches longer and contained oil grooves cut into their bore between the air ports and the base. These retained oil for a matching groove in the piston to take beyond the air belt to assist upper sleeve lubrication.

ing the movement around the cylinder centre-line. The shaded
eccentric (forming one of the crank webs) with its offset centre.
doing so the sleeve attachment spherical joint moves from right
g-end controlling piston movement. Note also (diagram 5) that,
sion takes place.

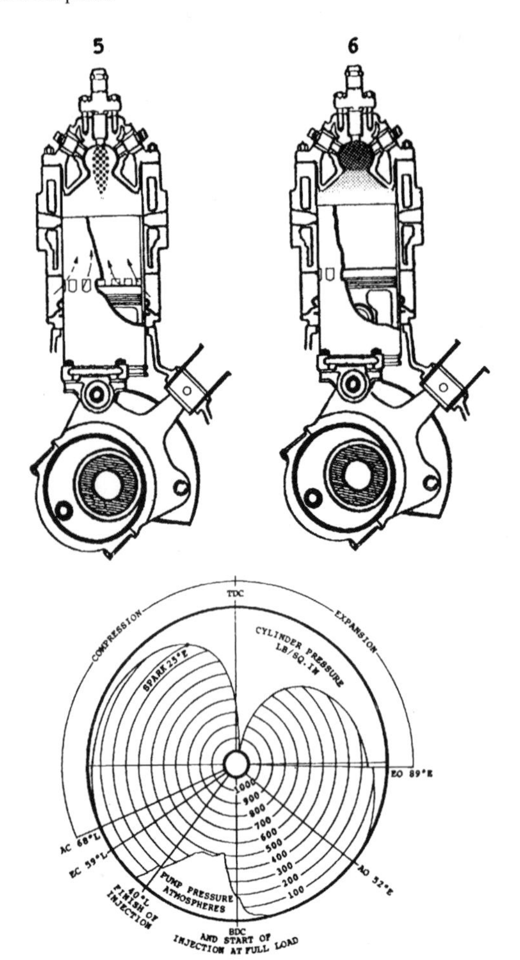

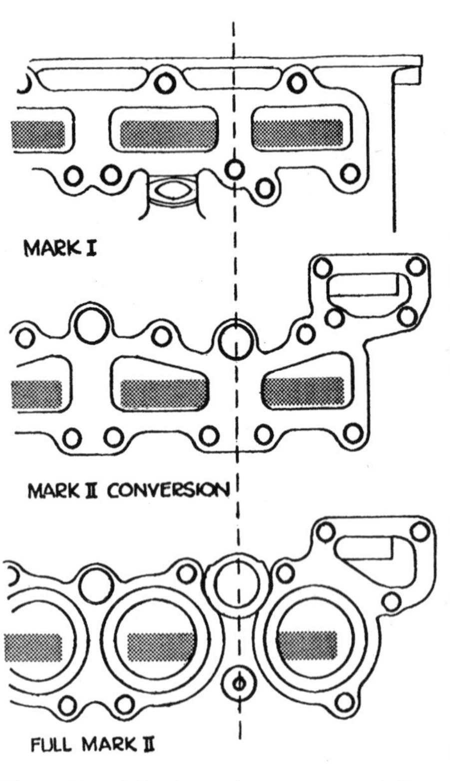

The profiles of the three exhaust outer port designs. At top is the original Mk.I design, the centre view is of the interim Mk.II an d at the bottom the circular shape of the Mk.II. In all views the divided exhaust port at its interior can be seen.

The working cycle of the Crecy. An understanding of the sleeve and piston motion relationships is obtained by obser
circle is the crankshaft and main-bearing which never deviates from the centre-line. The large surrounding circle is the
As the crankshaft rotates the eccentric, turning within the eccentric strap, causes the sleeve to rise and fall; note that in
to left to give a twist to the travel describing an elipse in the full cycle. The small circle close to the crankshaft is the b
unlike a four-stroke engine, the piston travels up the cylinder some way (until the air ports are closed) before compres

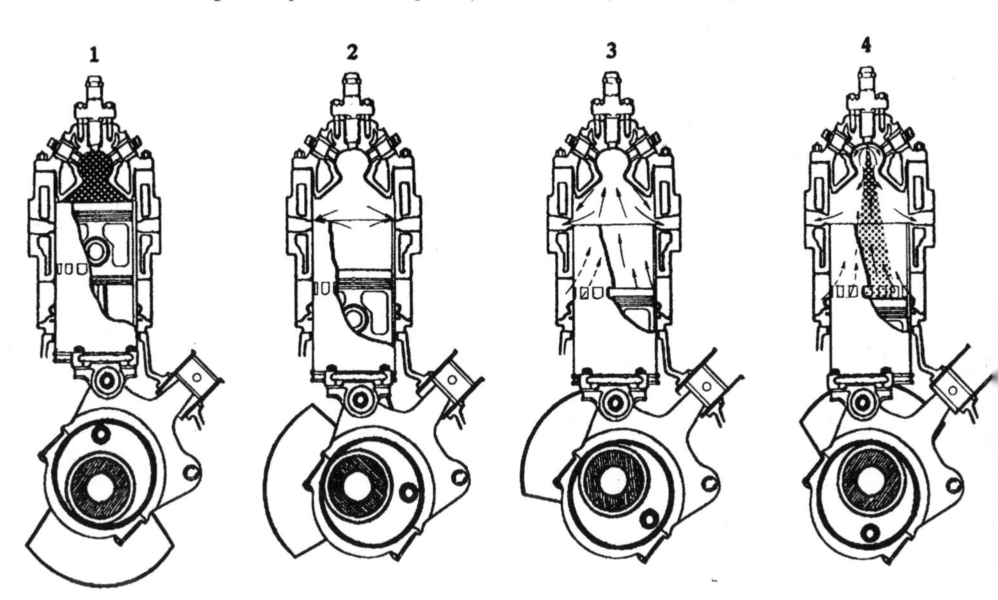

1. TOP DEAD CENTRE: Piston at top. Sleeve has commenced its downward stroke 15° ahead of crank.
2. EXHAUST OPENS 89° BEFORE BDC: Top edge of sleeve cuts across cylinder ports. Piston skirt is open to air blast for cooling.
3. AIR OPENS 52° BEFORE BDC: Top edge of piston cuts across the sleeve ports. Sleeve and piston travelling downwards. Scavenging commences. Exhaust ports are 3/4 open. Incoming air cools rings and top of piston. Air entering before injection commences sweeps in a vertical column to clean out bulb of exhaust residuals; termed 'half-loop scavenging'.
4. BOTTOM DEAD CENTRE: Injection commences (full load). Extreme end of spray catches air as it enters and eddies around the sleeve port bars breaking up the fuel particles.
5. EXHAUST CLOSES 59° AFTER BDC: Injection ends with rich dribble. Top edge of ascending sleeve closes cylinder ports. Cylinder filling takes place until boost pressure is attained.
6. AIR CLOSES 68° AFTER BDC: Top edge of piston cuts across the sleeve ports. Sleeve and piston moving upwards. Compression commences with rich mixture in bulb.

Timings calculated from bottom edge of chamfer on piston top.

ROLLS-ROYCE PI-26 CRECY ENGINE OPERATING CYCLE

The Crecy Mk.II engine. The most noticeable differences from the Mk.I are the vertical magneto housing and the coiled injector feed pipes. The diameter of each coil was such that the circumference equalled the distance between each injector. In this photograph all injectors and sparking plugs are connected to their pipes and leads. The exhaust ports now protrude from the face of the block and are circular in section as opposed to those on the Mk.I which were angular. This feature was part of Spike Corbitt's Crecy gas dynamics to reduce the exhaust temperature by about 80 degrees. It also allowed a flexible connection between the ports and the manifold

Performance

On 21 December 1944 Crecy No.10 attained the highest power measured from a main engine, 1798 bhp and 2350 shp, thus demonstrating the first design rating. This performance was without the turbine and when adjusted for inlet and exhaust testbed pressure losses converts to 1850 bhp in a flight configuration. Assuming turbine power would exceed blower power, the power would have been about 2500 hp with a turbine. The fuel loops during which this performance was recorded are illustrated.

A fuel loop is obtained by varying the fuel flow while operating the engine at a fixed blower throttle setting and RPM to maintain a constant boost pressure and airflow. The fuel loop is created by varying the fuel input in steps between maximum power and minimum specific fuel consumption at the particular RPM and taking readings at each step along the loop. In the Crecy the fuel flow was set by the fuel pump rack position under the control of the test operator and adjusted by a linkage from the control room.

The illustrated fuel loops were run at 2200, 2400 and 2600 rpm, with a single reading at 2800 rpm. It was this single reading that gave the maximum recorded power of a Crecy of 1798 bhp as mentioned above. At 2600 and 2800 rpm the interest was in high power and the lower ranges of powers were not investigated. At 2200 and 2400 rpm, economy was of concern and the loops were continued to the minimum specific fuel consumption occuring at 80 and 84% of maximum power respectively. The loop at 2200 rpm is shown extended below minimum fuel consumption with throttle wide open (solid line), with economy worsening. The worsening was accompanied by misfiring, vibration and, if extended further, by engine surge and cutting out. A broken line on the graph shows the trend when the

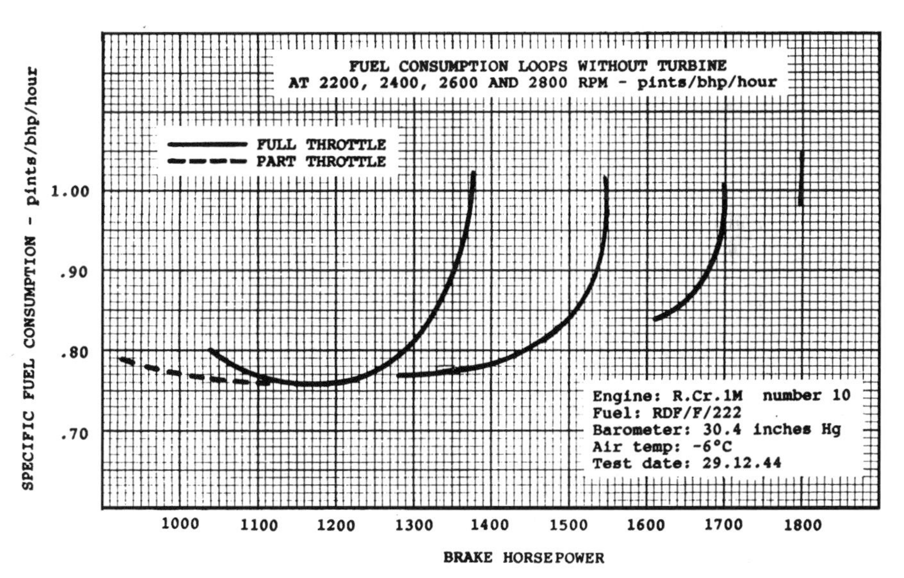

blower was throttled, reducing boost pressure and air flow, to stay at an air-to-fuel ratio of about 23 which gave the best economy and smooth operation. Finding the most efficient blower throttle setting (boost pressure, air flow) was very easy as it was the setting which gave the most power at the particular pump rack setting (fuel flow).

The shape of a Crecy loop is very different to that of a four-cycle loop. A four-cycle misfires and cuts out if fuel is weakened appreciably below about 98% of max power in the range of air-to-fuel ratio of about 14. Fuel input to the Crecy could be reduced until power was 75-80% of max power and an air/fuel ratio of 25 without turbine and 30 with turbine, without reduction of airflow and boost pressure, while maintaining smooth steady operation. The air/fuel ratios were higher with the turbine because longer port openings were used to increase airflow and reduce exhaust temperature. Below this figure the blower had to be throttled to maintain smooth and steady powers with simultaneous reduction of air and fuel. With the port openings used in the engines without the turbine best economy was achieved at an air-to-fuel ratio of about 23; maximum power occurred at about 15. The four-cycle engines would only operate within a narrow range of air-to-fuel ratio of about 12-14. When the turbine was fitted the ports were widened to obtain lower exhaust temperatures and the air/fuel ratios for best efficiency and max power became 25 and 30. Provided the engines were operated between air/fuel ratios for max power and minimum specific fuel consumption they ran smoothly and steadily at powers down to zero with simultaneous reduction of air and fuel.

Erratic running and excessive vibration occurred if the mixture strength was reduced significantly below max economy. The range of air-to-fuel ratio between max power and max economy provided an ample margin in which to operate and was much wider than any other petrol engine. During the relatively brief running accomplished with an exhaust turbine, operation was confined to engine exhaust/turbine inlet temperatures below 750°C whereas the temperature at maximum power was above 900°C. As a result of this temporary restriction the power measured with the turbine was less than had been obtained without it. The economy with the turbine was significantly better than without. At 2400 rpm best economy without turbine was .71 pts/hp/hr and with turbine .58 pts/hp/hr, an 18% improvement. At 1800 crankshaft rpm with the turbine a specific consumption of .55 pints/hp/hr was obtained.

At the end of the development the vee-twins were running well and demonstrating operation at over 250 bmep at 3000 rpm which would have given over 3000 bhp on a V12 engine (see Appendix I). The main engines completed two 112-hour flight approval tests including operation with a propellor.

The last run of a main engine occurred in December of 1945. The Crecy never flew.

Testing

The Crecy department included a design and drafting office, evacuated to Belper for most of the war, a development office and the engine testbeds which remained in Derby. At first there was one bed for the Ricardo E.65 single-cylinder engine and three vee-twin test beds, all surrounded by the four-cycle single-cylinder beds, and all located adjacent to the Experimental Shop at Nightingale Road . When the first main engine was built in 1941, Harry Wood was assigned a main-engine bed at Sinfin. Existing development facilities were used for the Crecy where possible, for example George 'Knocker' West's electrical laboratory, Alf Towle's mechanical component test laboratory and Geoff Wilde's supercharger test rigs. Where facilities were not available, for example, for fuel-injection pumps and injectors, they were established within the Crecy department.

The servicing and calibration of the fuel-injection pumps was an operation within the Crecy department in a small hut located near the twin-cylinder beds. Ken Wightman ran the injection pump rig and for a few months the author was his assistant. The pump on test was driven by an electric motor and a variable-speed belt drive. The 100-octane petrol discharging from the injection nozzles at 3000 psi was collected in measuring flasks. This operation produced copious petrol fumes and one could easily become inebriated by them. The injection-pump rig was in a small shed with thin, corrugated asbestos walls and roof on a steel frame, the better to destruct should there be an explosion. This was only one example of nonchalance towards fire hazards; floors were regularly washed with petrol and waste petrol was disposed of down the drains. On one occasion a cigarette butt was extinguished by being flicked into a bucket of petrol. There were the occasional fires in the trenches under engines at Sinfin which would be extinguished by the testbed fan and a squirt from an extinguisher, but never a serious one!

On the twin-cylinder beds the testers stood alongside the engine. The power control was at the injection pump, the dynamometer load was regulated with a hand wheel and the fuel consumption was measured by a stopwatch and a volume flask. Temperatures were partially indicated on an instrument board with remote measurement and partially by glass thermometers installed in various pipes connected to the engine. All data was recorded manually every 30 minutes during an endurance test or at intervals of about 5 minutes on a fuel loop or other parametric test. Results were calculated by slide-rule; not like today with computer logging!

All personnel worked very long hours during the war and Experimental Test worked the longest, as testing was non-stop 24-hours a day with two 12-hour shifts. When on an endurance test, meals were brought to the testbed from the canteen and eaten while operating the engine. The author remembers working 24 hours non-stop with Les Eggleston when the engine operation failed to agree with personnel scheduling, and 18 hours at a stretch was not unusual.

The Crecy main engines were tested at Sinfin when there were only four testbeds with dynamometers, three hangars for engines with propellors and a gun range at the site. At first the Crecy was tested on No.1 bed. Later this bed was changed to accommodate the Rolls-Royce industrial diesel engine, and Sinfin No.2 bed was changed to the Crecy. Crecy engines also ran with propellors on the Sinfin hangars on two occasions. When there were lulls between Crecys being available for test Griffons or Merlins would be run on the Crecy bed. This was a pain as it involved a major changeover of engine mounts and exhaust systems. The four-cycle engines would blacken the oil system, which stayed golden clean with the Crecy, and we would have to drain and clean the system before we ran a Crecy.

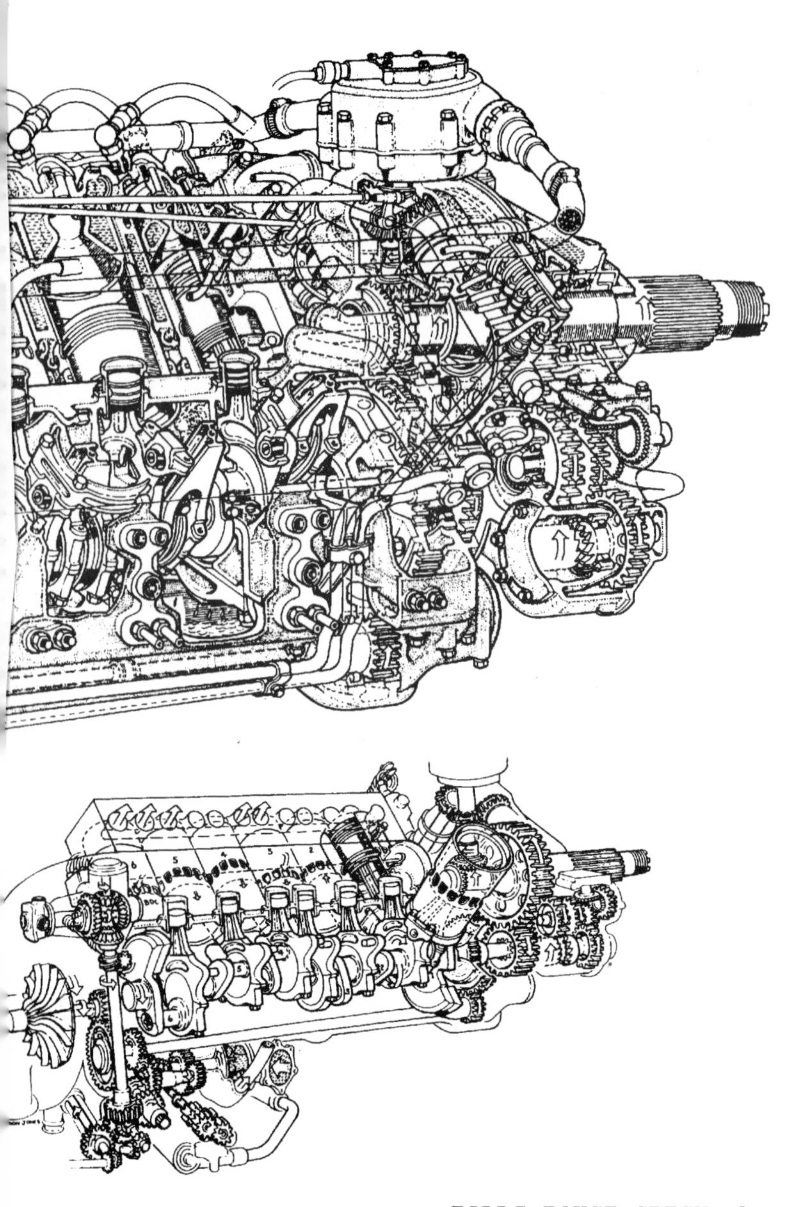

ROLLS-ROYCE CRECY Mk.II

ne early 1950's . The illustration was compiled solely from the photographs that appear in this book, study of scheme
al Department.

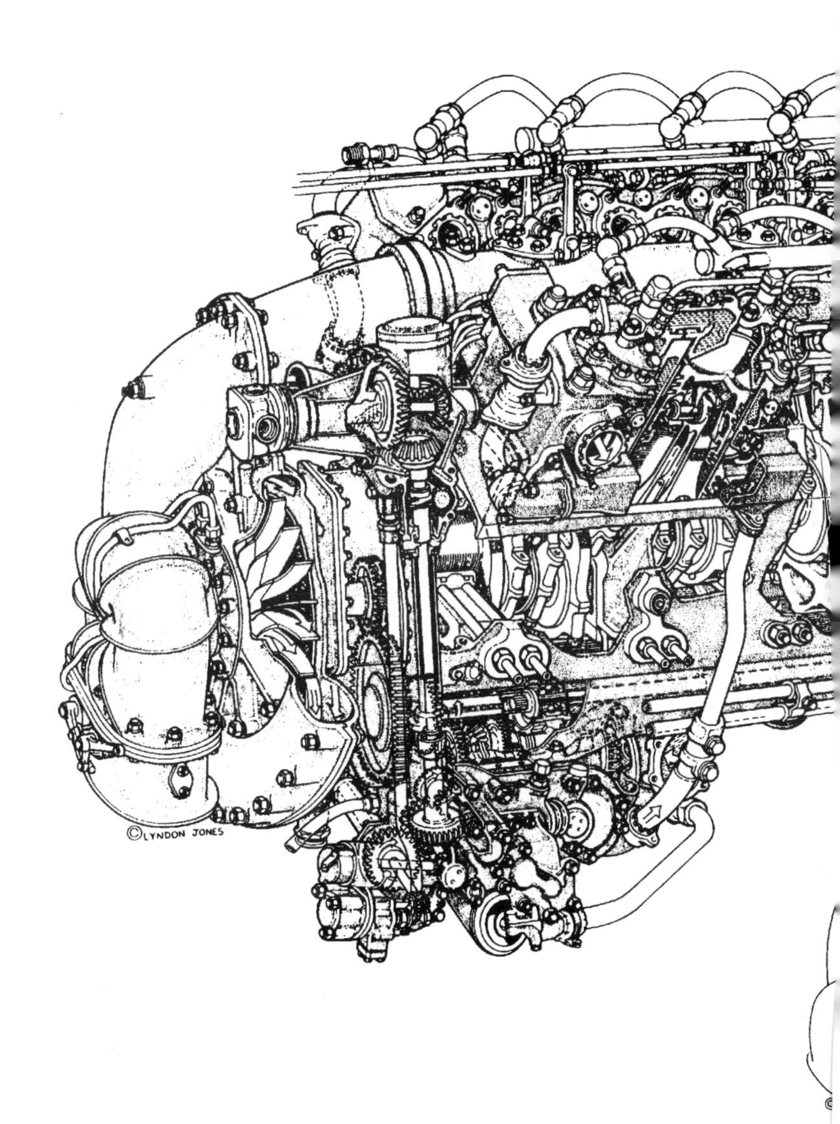

The superb cut-away drawing of the Crecy Mk.II by Lyndon Jones. The artist was a technical illustrator at Derby in
drawings of individual parts and the memory of Ken Fozard who, as an apprentice, assembled them in the Experime

All Crecy engines were constructed in the Nightingale Road Experimental Department. The single- and twin-engines were assembled under the supervision of Bill Holland. The main engines were erected by foreman Jack Marsden and his fitters including Cyril Baines, Frank Griffin, Frank Richardson and Ken Fozard. Additional to assembly of the engines in the shop, the fitters would come to the testbed to change magnetos or fuel-injection pumps, check or reset timing and take care of other problems. The testers were allowed to change injectors and sparking plugs, fuel-injector pipes which fractured frequently, and fix minor leaks.

During the whole period that the Crecy was on test all personnel in the Experimental shop did a great job repairing the engines after we had broken them on the testbeds. How they obtained replacement or redesigned parts so quickly was amazing, although some were robbed from other engines. Their co-operation was a pleasure throughout the whole era. No request of Jack Marsden and his fitters to change this or retime that was ever too much, and never an argument about getting the job done. The staff of the Experimental Shop gave the impression they really wanted this novel engine to work.

Engine performance was analysed by the development technical staff including Pat Lane, Geoff Waters and Joe Spooner. These gentlemen would come to the testbed to supervise tests in their area of responsibility.

Tests of piston-cooling oil flow were most unpleasant. For the test a main engine was modified to operate on one bank of cylinders. The cylinder heads of the other cylinder block were replaced by blanks without injectors, sparking plugs or cooling. The compression ratio of the blanked cylinders was increased to equal the normal firing gas pressure on the piston. Tubes connecting with the cooling oil passages were attached to special pistons and extended through the cylinder heads discharging the oil into collectors. From the collectors the oil was returned by a pump to the oil tank. A two-way valve was provided by which the oil could be diverted into a one-gallon container. The time for the gallon to fill was measured by stop watch from which the rate of flow was calculated. The exhaust ports on the bank being tested for oil flow were left open to the test bed without t he normal exhaust manifolds and the supercharged air mixed with leaked oil blasted out at the man doing the measuring. The fan which provided a 60 mph gale over the engine to cool exhaust stubs etc, was, of course, also running. In the blast of cooling air hot oil spilled everywhere. Oil would leak into the cylinders being tested for flow and at the high compression ratio, to balance the pressure on the piston, would ignite by compression ignition for a few cycles till the oil had burned off, with a sound like artillery and a blast of flame and smoke from the particular exhaust port. After one bank had been tested the engine was returned to the shop for the test equipment to be transferred to the other bank and the whole procedure repeated on the other six cylinders.

As described elsewhere, the oil flow would stop for up to ten seconds and then resume flowing. This probably was the reason for the unexplained piston failures but at the time we attributed the erratic flow to aberrations of the test equipment. The development engineers specified the piston oil flow tests and were responsible for supervising them and evaluating the results. They had the information to judge the significance of the interruption of the oil flow equally as much as we testers. The whole procedure of the oil flow test was so unpleasant that everyone was just glad to get it over with.

Outstanding problems

At the termination of development the main engines were still suffering random piston failures at the higher crankshaft speeds. It is the author's opinion that these failures were the result of air displacing the cooling oil in the drilled passage in the connecting-rod of the piston which failed. Without the cooling oil the piston overheated and seized in the sleeve.

The Ricardo single-cylinder units and the Rolls-Royce vee-twin units would run indefinitely at high powers. Operating the V-12 main engines at similar bmep caused random piston failures. These failures had to be caused by a difference between the single- and twin-cylinder and the 12-cylinder engines.

The failures only occurred at the higher rpm. Inertia increases as speed squared, thus an increase in rpm increased the capacity of the rods to pump the piston cooling oil proportional to speed squared. Oil was supplied to the crankshaft by a positive-displacement gear pump, thus the flow of oil was proportional to rpm. At higher rpm the pumping capacity of the rods probably exceeded the supply of oil from the pump passing through the crankshaft of the main engines. The oil reaching a big-end bearing probably could be pumped by the inertia forces in one of the two rods on a crank. When the oil pressure in a rod was reduced by the rod's pumping action the air entrained in the oil would expand and unprime one rod on a crank. The rod which remained primed would draw off all the oil flowing to the crank preventing the unprimed rod from being re-primed.

At lower rpm the pumping capacity of the rods would be less than the flow of oil through the crankshaft and even should a rod become air-locked the pressure and flow of oil from the pump would be sufficient to displace the air, re-prime the rod and restore the flow of cooling oil to the pistons before overheating occurred. Thus piston failures did not occur at lower rpm. This theory was supported by piston oil flow tests during which the flow to a piston would stop for up to 10 seconds. In 10 seconds a piston would be exposed to up to 400 firing strokes and it is understandable that a piston could overheat when this happened. The temporary cessation of oil flow during flow tests was attributed to bad test equipment. In retrospect it probably was air locking in the connecting rods and we were blind not to have realised it. It is my opinion that this was the likely reason for most if not all failures explained as 'sleeve failure, sleeve seizure, ring breakage and piston seizure', as the strip examination of engines following such incidents usually revealed a sameness about the damage. In the main engines the oil reached the crankshaft bearings by a tortuous path whereason the singles and twins the path was shorter and not constricted by the main engine features. The singles and twins were fitted with relatively large oil pumps. These differences explain why the singles and twins were free from this problem and the main engines were not.

Hives had insisted, over the objections of the Crecy design staff, that oil feed into both ends of the crankshaft be incorporated in the Crecy, as it had in the other Rolls-Royce engines, thus increasing the oil supply to the con-rods. I believe Hives was zeroing-in on the piston oil cooling problem by an intuitive sixth sense which he seemed to possess. I recommend to future developers of high-speed engines that they do not rely on oil feed to the pistons through the crankshaft and connecting rods. An oil jet spraying at the piston crown seems equally effective, is less complicated and subject to fewer uncertainties.

Piston failures were the major mechanical weakness remaining in the basic engine when development was terminated. There were many problems with auxiliary equipment which could have been solved with adequate priority. The magnetos were a continuing source of trouble. Frequent petrol injection pipe failures needed a solution. The Crecy required very high torque to turn it over and get it started because of the large area of oil film around the sleeves. We found no flight-capable starter able to start it on a cold Sinfin day, not Coffman, not inertia, and not with 48 volts applied to a 24-volt electric motor.

The exhaust turbine was still in a shakedown phase and had not been operated at any significant power. A system for operation of the Crecy with a single power lever, as would be required in an aircraft, had not been developed.

There is little doubt that with further development the Crecy would have achieved its projected ratings. The power output for the relatively small frontal area would have been phenomenal. Aircraft like the Spitfire or the Mustang with a Crecy would have been outstanding. With an exhaust turbine the Crecy would have been well suited to slower, heavy-lift bomber or transport aircraft. The superior specific fuel consumption with a turbine would have increased range or allowed a heavier payload.

During the whole period in which the Crecy was under development forecasts of its potential performance were highly favourable. For example, an evaluation by the Royal Aircraft Establishment is related in a letter to Harry Wood in May of 1944. In the evaluation the Crecy, with an exhaust turbine, is compared with a jet, a turbo-prop and a four-cycle engine. The study rated the Crecy potentially superior to its competition on all counts except in the single criterion of combined weight of power plant and fuel in which the Crecy was second only to a hypothetical turbo-prop, and by only 100 lb in 5000 lb. (At the time of the report no turbo-props had yet been built).

The superiority in total weight projected for the turbo-prop was the 'writing on the wall' for the development of piston aero-engines. In June of 1945 a confidential report was issued by Farnborough in which the performance of the Crecy fitted with an axial compressor and exhaust turbine was predicted. (It is interesting to note that the Napier Nomad two-stroke diesel, ten years later, used an axial-flow compressor and exhaust turbine). The report predicted an engine, plus turbine, minus compressor power of 5700 bhp for take-off and 5500 bhp at 500 mph and 20,000 ft. This is 475 bhp per cylinder. No other aircraft engine approached this output.

The distribution of this report is interesting as listing those interested in, or involved in, the Crecy including most of the scientific and research heads along with Ricardo, Penn of Napier, Wood and Lovesey of Rolls-Royce, Robinson of the Admiralty and Constant of the RAE.

J H Pitchford successively was Technical Director, Managing Director and Chairman of Ricardo & Co. In a paper presented in 1960 he discussed the performance potential of the Crecy and included one of the few illustrations of the engine which have been published. I will quote from his paper verbatim:-

"The piston aero-engine, was perhaps the finest version of the reciprocating engine designed for a specialised purpose. One interesting example of an engine in this category is the Rolls-Royce Crecy, which had just arrived at the 'flying test-bed' stage when the gas turbine supplanted it.

The Company [Ricardo] carried out the bulk of the early single-cylinder work which led to this development. The Crecy was a 60° [sic] vee-twelve-cylinder, single-sleeve valve, two-cycle engine. .... A feature of particular interest in this engine was that the single-sleeve valves were open-ended and did not seal in a cylinder head junk-ring but directly against the cylinder bores, once they had risen on the upward stroke above the top edge of the exhaust ports. .... Another point of interest in this engine was the achievement of a degree of stratified charge operation by virtue of the proximity of the cone of the central fuel spray to the sparking plugs. The cone angle of the spray at light loads increased markedly as compared with full load, so that with small injections the fringe of the spray was directed at the two sparking plugs, maintaining a roughly constant mixture strength in the region of ignition and within wide limits, throughout the separate combustion chamber. .... The engine weighed little more than the Merlin and had, of course, a very much greater power development potential.

When further work on the whole project was terminated because of the rapid development of the jet engine, the Company investigated, as a matter of technical interest, the ultimate power potential of the engine by taking one of the single-cylinder units installed at the Shoreham works up to its limit. The results are, I think, impressive: a gross output of 358 bhp was obtained at 4000 rev/min which is equivalent to 219 bhp/litre of cylinder capacity."

The Crecy stroke was 6.5 inch. At 4000 rpm the piston speed of the E.65 was 3833 ft/min. At the same piston speed and bmep the Crecy rpm would be 3538 and power would be 194 bhp per litre. With the assumption of turbine power equalling supercharger power the shaft power would be 5037 bhp. Has any four-cycle piston engine of equal weight or frontal area the potential to equal the output predicted by Farnborough, demonstrated by Ricardo and reported by Pitchford?

Crecy personnel

Harry Wood, FRAeS, Whitworth Scholar, assumed responsibility for the two-cycle diesel project soon after he joined the Company. He later was also responsible for the conversion of the Merlin to a marine engine for motor gun boats. This responsibility was soon handed to Lionel Haworth. He received his technical training through a Whitworth Scholarship. When the Crecy programme folded he was appointed head of the marine gas turbine project for the Royal Navy.

Wood was a charming and approachable gentleman and was eager to discuss viewpoints with anyone. To a young test engineer he seemed very formidable but the writer used to drop into his office and discuss problems with the engine. He was the only senior person in the organisation whom I could engage in an informal technical discussion. A retrospective judgement is that he was good at administration and liaison with the funding ministries and others. Engineering and personnel

Harry Wood was the Chief Engineer over the Crecy project. Born in 1892 he served his apprenticeship as an engine fitter at the Sheerness dockyard followed by a three-year course in civil and mechanical engineering at City and Guilds. In 1934 he joined the Experimental Department at Rolls-Royce and became responsible for the direction of single-cylinder research on liquid- and air-cooled units along with fuel investigation. In 1938 he began research and development on two-stroke compression-ignition engines. He also headed the Marine Division tasked with adapting the Merlin aero-engine to power boats for the coastal forces of the Royal Navy. In the following year he assumed responsibility for research, design and development of two-stroke petrol-injection engines. When the Crecy programme ended he took charge of compound gas turbines, in particular the RM.60 marine engine.

management were not his strength.

Responsibility for the Crecy was integrated with Merlin development and transferred from Wood to Lovesey in 1944. Lovesey's usual magic was not successful because of the very different features and operation of the Crecy compared to a four-cycle engine and the heavy demands on him by the never-ending development of the Merlin. Responsibility was returned to Wood after a few months.

Development and test of the Crecy engines was under the supervision of Wood through a chief development engineer who for most of the time was Dick Thomas (Wd/RHT), the equivalent of Lovesey in the much smaller department. He had responsibility for the test and development of the engines. He had held a similar position at Pobjoy before joining Rolls-Royce. (Pobjoy had, pre-war, produced a very neat small radial which was fitted in the Comper Swift and other aeroplanes.) In consultation with the design office Dick Thomas and his personnel planned tests, analysed performance, diagnosed failures, prescribed fixes and issued reports of progress.

Dick had a strong personality and was a character. On one occasion a vee-twin was on test and was discharging a lot of lubricating oil from the exhaust onto the roof of the test house. This oil caught fire and though there was no danger the fire was very conspicuous in the blackout. Dick grabbed a fire extinguisher and clambered up a ladder to the roof before the works' fire brigade had arrived. The firemen wanted to take over fighting the fire but Dick blocked the ladder and would not climb down shouting "this is my fire".

During a very hot spell of weather Dick came to work in shorts and stopped work in the Experimental Shop as he walked through, accompanied by cat calls, banging on metal cans, etc. He never did it again!

If the Crecy had lived up to the extravagant claims of Dick Thomas it would have been in squadron service by the end of hostilities. When the Crecy project was returned from Lovesey to Harry Wood's jurisdiction Dick departed the Company and Spike Corbitt assumed the duties of chief development engineer.

Staff in the Crecy development office under Dick Thomas were Ron Brain, Colin Hewson, Pat Lane, Joe Spooner, Peter Stuttard, Geoff Waters and Les Worn.

Ron Brain was an engineering apprentice and obtained his London University B.Sc at Derby Tech. Ron ran the Crecy fuel system development and subsequently the RM.60 marine engine fuel and combustion systems. He later became Chief Development Engineer on the RZ.2 rocket engine for Blue Streak.

Colin Hewson was an engineering apprentice and as part of the Crecy team followed the author as liaison engineer with Ricardo in Oxford for several months. Subsequently he worked on direct-lift engines and was the Rolls-Royce representative at MTU in Germany.

Pat Lane came to Rolls-Royce from university as an engineering pupil and was responsible for piston cooling oil flow tests on main engines. He later transferred to Merlin development after a couple of years under Dick Thomas.

Joe Spooner was a Ph.D and made extensive performance analyses and predictions. Joe left Rolls-Royce to join the Engineering faculty of Manchester University. There was talk of a vee-twin engine being donated to the University for Joe's use when the Crecy project folded. Perhaps it is still there in a remote corner of a laboratory.

Peter Stuttard was an engineering apprentice and worked in the department during its transition from CI to PI in an office close to the old metallurgical laboratory. Peter did stints on twin-cylinder engine testing and then transferred to Lionel Howarth's drawing office where he worked on the Dart. Peter later wrote many of the workshop manuals for the post-war cars. Peter has since managed a garage and been an industrial insurance adjuster.

Geoff Waters was a graduate engineer and worked on Crecy development also under Wd/RHT. Geoff was responsible for records of all main engines.

Les Worn worked on the project when it was compression-ignition. After a short stint he transferred to the supercharger department under Geoff Wilde. Les left Rolls-Royce for Plessey.

R W 'Spike' Corbitt (Rg/Cbt) served his apprenticeship with the Great Western Railway at Swindon, was a Whitworth Scholar and came to Rolls-Royce from the Admiralty. He was a personal assistant to Rowledge (Rg) before becoming Crecy development head. Rowledge had earlier designed the Napier Lion engine which many thought was superior to the competing Rolls-Royce engines in the 1920-30 era.

Spike's forte was thermo-gas-dynamics and there was a story that Spike had improved the Merlin's breathing by airflow tests of a model of a Merlin port using his landlady's vacuum cleaner. I have since copied Spike by using industrial vacuum cleaners to conduct aerodynamic tests. Spike was a frustrated supercharger designer and was a 'pain' to the supercharger department with all his ideas for better superchargers. Following his gas dynamic philosophy he was the major advocate of piston cooling by airflow through the cylinder and placed little importance on oil cooling of the pistons. Others felt oil cooling was the more important. After the Crecy job folded Spike assumed responsibility for development of the Rolls-Royce marine gas turbine, the RM.60. He passed away in 1989.

R W 'Spike' Corbitt, seen here at the time he was working on the Crecy. Clever though he was, his belief that the pistons could be sufficiently cooled by air alone could never be seen by others to be justified either practically or theoretically.

Les Eggleston came to Rolls-Royce from Pobjoy where he had worked with Dick Thomas and was engaged in Crecy testing from beginning to end of the project. Les was conscientious and fun to work with. During the Battle of Britain there was a backup of Merlin engines needing overhaul and Les became an inspector of repair Merlins for a few months. Early in 1945 he took charge of running the twin-cylinder engines and the writer became supervisor of main-engine testing at Sinfin. With the demise of the Crecy, Les left to take charge of maintenance for a Middle East airline. Les was a strong Cockney and had many stories to tell of racing a Chater Lee motor-cycle at Brooklands. Others involved in twin-cylinder engine test included Harry Noble who was a kind of charge-hand and Jack Steer who was a kind of foreman. When Harry came around the test beds about one hour after starting time he would watch what I was doing and then tell me to do it!

Dick Foster-Pegg (Wd/RFP) – the co-author – joined Rolls-Royce in September 1937 from public school as one of the first engineering apprentices. As an apprentice I worked in more departments than any other apprentice and on graduation received the usual certificate signed by Hives and 'Tubby' Ward. Prior to completion of my apprenticeship I was assigned to the Two-Stroke Division. My first job in the PI department was testing fuel pumps. I graduated to assistant tester on twin engines and later took full charge of a twin test bed. Les Eggleston and I were assigned to test the main engines at Sinfin. Except for a short period in 1944 the writer was involved in all the Crecy main-engine testing. Les became supervisor of vee-twin testing in 1945 and I took over supervision of main-engine testing. I was appointed inspector for the Aeronautical Inspection Directorate (AID). It was standard practice for company employees to also serve as inspectors, but it seemed like setting a thief to catch a thief. I was the first representative of the Rolls-Royce Crecy operation assigned to Ricardo. At the time Ricardo were evacuated from Shoreham to a garage in Oxford.

When Lovesey took over from Wood I worked in Alf Arnold's experimental testing office for a short period, writing test schedules and calculating performance. I found this unchallenging and arranged a transfer to Geoff Wilde's supercharger test. Most of the testing was at night when the electric power to drive the rigs was available. I worked on the night shift and learned a lot about superchargers. When Wood retook control of the Crecy department I returned in charge of Crecy main-engine testing. Others involved in Crecy main engine testing were Ted Wright, who transferred from production engine test, and Jack Piggs. Bob Brown ran test rigs and twin engines.

I had almost no contact with the Crecy design office. I can remember Chief Designer Eddie Gass occasionally looking in on an engine test and I got to know Frank Stark who was Assistant Chief Designer. Billy Butler, Dr Bauer, Harry Darbyshire and Ken Herbert were also in the design office. I never knew these gentlemen. When the Crecy project folded I stayed under Wood in charge of testing the RM.60 marine gas turbine.

From Rolls-Royce I went to McGill University in Canada at the invitation of the late Donald Mordell, where I supervised the operation of a Rolls-Royce Dart fuelled by coal. Subsequent employment has included American Locomotive, Bechtel, Struthers Wells and Westinghouse. I am presently an independent consultant on gas turbine and steam power plants.

Lionel Haworth worked on compression-ignition in the pre Crecy days when the office was on the top floor of No.6 shop. Lionel worked there with Wood, Dick Thomas and Eddie Gass and designed Rowledge's linear-motion, crank-driven, sleeve-drive mechanism which only saw use on the CI V-twins prior to their conversion to the eccentric sleeve-drive. Harry Wood was responsible for both the CI and the marine conversion of the Merlin. The dual responsibility was detrimental to both jobs so Hives gave the marine engine to Lionel and left Wood with the CI.

Frank Stark and his wife Gladys were among the most friendly and enjoyable people. Frank had worked on the Merlin prior to leaving to work with the famous W O Bentley on the design of the Lagonda V.12 motor car. He returned to Derby in 1938. At the

Eddie Gass, the Crecy's designer. He is seen here at the time he was a draughtsman in the Merlin detail design office in 1936, no doubt oblivious to future events that would see him being responsible for the design of one of the world's most fascinating and inovative aero-engines. He died in 1950.

time of the V1 Flying Bomb attacks he constructed a ramjet engine from a cylinder head and carburettor from a motor-cycle and a piece of pipe. He operated this device, which sounded like a rapid-firing artillery gun, in his yard in Chellaston, to the chagrin of his neighbours. Speaking in 1971 he recalled the following about his time with the Crecy:

"Early in 1938 I had a letter from Denning Pearson, who said in effect, "stop playing around with sporty motor cars and come back to Derby and do some serious work". I wrote back to him leaving the door open and he said there was an interesting project coming up with the firm. They were starting up a new design office to deal with this project and why not come and have a talk about it? I went to Derby and found that the project was a two-stroke aircraft engine, a big one. This was to use the open-ended sleeve-valve that Ricardo had developed, building it into a 12-cylinder, V-type water-cooled engine – a supercharged diesel.

"Before we really got launched on that, and while we were getting together a design staff, we did a marine version of the Merlin engine for Scott Paine for his motor torpedo boat, just before the war. This was for me a useful introduction to marine practice.

We then started on this 12-cylinder two-stroke engine and it was then that I really had anything to do with Rowledge, because at that time he was design consultant to this Two-stroke Division. He was near retirement and, in effect, he had passed his responsibilities for aircraft engines to Elliott, who was then controlling the Merlin design work as well as the cars. Rowledge's only other interest was in an engine known as the 'Exe', which was a 24-cylinder, X-type, air-cooled four-stroke with a conventional sleeve, junkhead and all the associated mechanisms.

Frank Stark

"This was really my first connection with sleeve-valve engines. I had no dealings at all with the Daimler [motor car] sleeve-valve engine, which was a dreadful engine, but all sleeve-valve engines are, in my opinion, dreadful engines. I had an instinctive dislike of them but I think at the time nobody really appreciated that with a sleeve-valve, even a single sleeve, how difficult it is to get heat out of the piston into the cooling water of the engine, or whatever the cooling medium is. With a single sleeve heat has got to pass through two oil films and this is a very considerable difficulty. Sir Roy Fedden was a sleeve-valve protagonist, but his was the junkhead conventional sleeve. The penny never dropped with him.

"This engine started off as a diesel,

but immediately the war commenced it was switched to petrol-injection with spark ignition and then it really became a very exciting piece of mechanism. I think, perhaps, that the evolution of the design contained an indication of Rowledge's bigness as an engineer. He designed the sleeve drive by running a little crankshaft along the side of the engine with a little crank throw for each sleeve and a little underslung connecting-rod for propelling this sleeve up and down. The travel of the sleeve was about 1.6 inches and Rowledge very cleverly used the obliquity of the connecting rod to get very rapid opening of the exaust port. [In actual fact this sleeve drive was designed by Lionel Haworth who, like everyone else, worked for Harry Wood. Rowledge, though, was a frequent visitor to the design office on the top floor of No.6 shop.- Editor]

"In the meantime, I had entered the sleeve-drive business with a crank-drive mechanism that I had thought of, which operated from an eccentric at each crank throw; one of the two webs. It was a large eccentric, which carried a strap and a little guide crosshead piston and two arms with connections to each of the two sleeves, so that the one eccentric drove the two sleeves of the cylinder that were associated with that particular crank pin. This was an extremely effective mechanism and eventually won out against Rowledge's system and the whole engine design was based on this mechanism.

"We worked on that engine through the war but when the question of production came up .... Hives decided to continue with the Merlin because its sound conception was being proved again and again. The other consideration was that the gas turbine was appearing on the horizon, so the Crecy project was abandoned. Half a dozen were made, and to hear the engine running on the testbed, at 15 lb boost and 3000 rpm, with open exhausts, was something never to be forgotten".

The following is a listing of those known to have been employed within the Two-stroke Division on Crecy design, development, assembly and test. There were others, for example, Geoff Wilde (supercharger performance) who did not work for the Division but were involved in some way or other.

Management.

Chief engineer:	Harry Wood, Cyril Lovesey

Design office.

Chief designer:	Eddie Gass
Senior designers:	Frank Gordon, Frank Stark
Designers:	Harold Blackburn, Cyril Blea (drives), Ken Bracey, John Buchan, Harry Darbyshire, George Stanley (injection pumps), Len Stapleford, Harry Sutcliffe (cylinder blocks), Lionel Haworth (1938-39 CI twin only)
Detailers:	Jack Blackwell, Bill Butler, Peter Dewsbury, Stan Evans, Marjory Gass, Stan Hardy, Paul Harrison, Ray Hart, Ken Herbert, Harry Hurdis, Jim Lewis, Ron Pike, Ron Richards, Jack Tyler, Frank Vaughan
Technical advisor:	Dr George Bauer
Typists:	Margaret Baxendale, Mary Bigley
Office boy:	John Butlin

Development office.

Chief engineers:	Dick Thomas, R W 'Spike' Corbitt
Engineers:	Ron Brain, Colin Hewson, Peter Stuttard, Geoff Waters, Les Worn
Testers:	Bob Brown, Les Eggleston, Dick Foster-Pegg, Jack Piggs, Jack Steer, Harry Noble (twin-cylinder), Ken Wightman (rigs)
Performance:	Pat Lane, Joe Spooner

Experimental Department build.

Crankcase:	Ernie Ball, J Fitzgerald
Supercharger and wheelcase:	Walter Holmes, Stan Hayes
Cylinders, sleeves and pistons:	George Dallison, William Clibbery
Controls:	Roland Metcalf, Walter Smith
Fuel pumps:	Bill Clay
Engine erection:	Cyril Baines, Ken Fozard, Frank Griffin, Bill Holland, Eric Marsden Jack Marsden, Frank Richardson
Single-cylinder engines:	Edward Brooks, Percy Brown, Victor Farthing, Jack Ryan

Some fitters worked on more than one particular section.

CHAPTER THREE

The unfulfilled promise

by David Birch

To those who know their aero-engines the Crecy has always portrayed an aura of immense interest, not to say mystique. This is partly due to the very secret nature of the project during its periods of conception and development. Very few people were 'in the know'. In 1942, Wood complained to Bill Lappin, Hives' liaison man to the ministries, military and aircraft constructors, that too many people in the industry were being informed of the Crecy's existence by visiting liaison engineers. He reminded him of the confidentiality that the project demanded.

Although only six engines were built, which spent all their days on the test bed, the story can be supplemented by a glimpse into what might have been. Had the Crecy been fully developed the results would have been spectacular. But it was not to be. The reasons for this are fourfold; lack of priority status, not enough qualified talent, development problems and the rapid acceptance of the gas turbine. If only Messrs Whittle and von Ohain had been born ten years later, what a glorious swansong there might have been for the piston aero-engine.

If the Crecy had flown it would have first done so in Hawker Henley L3385, which was delivered to Hucknall for conversion on 28 March 1943. By this time the Crecy was nearly two years old but a measure of the pace of development can be gauged from the fact that following engine failures during its first period of testing it was to be eight months before it ran again. Nevertheless, it must have been thought that the engine was approaching the flight trials stage for the Henley to be delivered. Wishful thinking as it turned out. The Henley hung around Hucknall like a jilted bridegroom before being dismantled and disposed of on 11 September 1945.

This frustrated conversion was not Hucknall's first involvement with the Crecy. In the summer of 1941 the fuselage of Spitfire II P7674 was fitted with a Crecy mock-up to enable the drawing office to establish cowling lines and other installation features. At this time there was interest in this combination following a meeting at Hucknall in the July in which it had been agreed that the first production Spitfire III would be delivered to Hucknall early in 1942, without an engine, and fitted with the Crecy. This never happened, as indeed the production Spitfire III never happened, and the flying testbed was put on ice for two years. If nothing else this shows the confidence that Rolls-Royce and the Air Ministry had in the engine at that time which only had a few hours running behind it. The Spitfire III was aerodynamically much cleaner than previous marks and its marriage to the Crecy would have been an interesting exercise. This interest was still prevalent one year later when Witold Challier, Hucknall's chief performance engineer, predicted the performance of the Spitfire IV with the Crecy.

The report, dated 14 June 1942, and based on a similar report (No.E.3932) issued by the Royal Aircraft Establishment at Farnborough, concluded that its findings depended to a large extent upon the accuracy with which the characteristics of the two-stroke engine had been estimated. Three sets of figures were given based on the assumptions of power forecast by the RAE and Rolls-Royce, the former also quoting a two-stage supercharged version. This of course, was before the advent of the exhaust turbine and with the engine ope rating at its then maximum speed of 2750 rpm.

	Single-stage RAE power	Two-stage RAE power	Single-stage RR power	Spitfire HF.IX
AUW (lb)	8,700	9,200	8,700	7,395
Top Speed at SL (mph)	352	325	341	319
Top Speed at FTH	431 at 18,500	468 at 32,100	440 at 24,500	410 at 28,000
Absolute Ceiling (ft)	42,100	45,500	43,300	42,600
Service Ceiling (ft)	41,100	44,800	42,600	42,200
Operational Ceiling (ft)	38,200	41,900	39,500	40,200
Rate of Climb at SL (ft/min)	3,660	2,760	3,310	3,810

The average Spitfire IX figures with a Merlin 61 operating at 15 lb boost are included for comparison as this was the latest fighter to enter service with the RAF at that time.

Challier's comments at the end of the report are worth reproducing. "It will be seen that the estimated performance is very high, both speed and ceiling. The high speed is due to the large ejector thrust power which is much greater than in a four-stroke engine and amounts to over 35% of the engine power at high speeds and altitudes. The two-stroke engine is thus another step forward in the direction of a propulsive unit combining the advantages of jet propulsion - high thrust at high speeds, with the advantages of airscrew propulsion - high thrust at low speeds, which is important for take-off and climb.

"The high ceiling is due to the fact that the estimated variation of the two-stroke brake horsepower above the full throttle height (FTH) is more favourable than the power variation of the four-stoke engine. The density law seems to be a good approximation up to some 42,000 feet and it is rather interesting that this same law is followed by the indicated horsepower of the four-stroke engine. If the estimated power variation is confirmed by flight tests, the ceiling of fighter aircraft could be improved by some 3000 feet by fitting two-stroke engines of similar power and full throttle height. The low-altitude performance is good due to the increase of power obtained by using the vortex throttle".

This device, which only appeared on the Crecy, gave pre-swirl to the air before it entered the supercharger rotor so that the entry angle was reduced from around 60° to about 30°. This was Spike Corbitt's idea, one which he had brought back from a pre-war visit to Sydlowski in France. All Crecy engines had it but for some reason (and to Spike's disgust) it wasn't considered for any other piston engine. Like all good ideas it was so simple. The two throttle butterflies were located north-south across the inside of the intake instead of east-west. Thus whenever the engine was throttled to develop a power less than maximum the air passing them was deflected to create a swirl angle to enhance its entry into the supercharger rotor. At maximum power, of course, with the butterflies wide open and vertical in their intake bores, there was no aerodynamic advantage over the conventional configuration.

The RAE preliminary performance estimate of a Crecy-powered Spitfire was issued in March 1942. By August of the same year an addendum, (see Appendix I) was issued in the light of a better understanding of the two-stroke's characteristics. The original report compared the Crecy Spitfire with a Griffon II-powered variant - the Mk IV. With the forthcoming availability of the two-stage supercharged Griffon 61 a new comparison was made with what would emerge as the Spitfire XIV. Whenever possible the parameters were adjusted in order to compare each engine's performance at a common full throttle height and rpm.

Again, Farnborough based its figures on a two-stage supercharged Crecy, a hypothetical configuration that never achieved reality and probably never would have. As we have seen the Company opted to retain the single-stage, single-speed blower and go for an exhaust turbine. However, these were early days for the Crecy and it was logical thinking by the RAE that its performance would eventually be enhanced, like the Merlin and Griffon, by two-stage supercharging. In both cases the engines were considered to be driving six-bladed contra-rotating propellors.

		True Air Speed (MPH)			
		Griffon 61		Two-stroke	
Super-charger gear	Altitude (feet)	Without exhaust thrust	With exhaust thrust	Without exhaust thrust	With exhaust thrust
MS	5,000	345	351	343	366
	13,500 FTH	388	400	378	408
	23,500	373	399	371	403
FS	31,500 FTH	419	454	400	471
	40,000	377	424	372	460

These figures show a near agreement with each other, taking into account the contrived full throttle heights. It is worth remembering that the Griffon had a capacity of 37 litres whereas the Crecy was only 26 litres. The most interesting aspect of the figures is the effect on speed by the thrust from the exhaust stubs. At the lower altitude it contributed 6 mph to the Griffon Spitfire's top speed whereas its competitor enjoyed a 23 mph increase. At 40,000 feet jet thrust was responsible for 47 and 88 mph respectively. The benefit of the two-stroke's double exhaust energy is obvious. So too is the fact that when the supercharger begins to lose its efficiency, with the resultant loss in speed above the FTH, the thrust from the two-stroke is much better than the four-stroke in helping to regain the loss. Note that the Griffon loses 30 mph between FTH and 40,000 feet whereas the two-stroke only loses 11 mph. If these figures are impressive, what came next in the report was truly incredible.

The RAE version of the Rolls-Royce two-stroke engine (it is not really fair to refer to it as the Crecy even though Farnborough's extrapolations were aimed at that engine) was given a brake mean effective pressure figure of 200 lb/sq.in, which was reasonable as the Crecy at that time was not far short of it. (Brake Mean Effective Pressure (bmep) is the pressure in pounds per square inch which , if exerted on the piston for the full stroke, would produce the power measured by the dynamometer (brake) with zero frictional losses. For equivalent power output the bmep of a two-stroke is worth twice the same bmep in a four-stroke. Hence two-stroke bmep is often written 'x 2' – say 225 (x2), equal to 450 in a four-stroke). Its maximum engine operating speed was 2750 rpm, which was identical to the Griffon. Air consumption was adjudged to be a minimum of 1.1 times that of the volume of the cylinder, a seemingly low figure for the two-stroke when compared to the 1.5 times swept volume achieved by the single-stage supercharged Crecy (ie. enough air enters the cylinder to fill it 1.5 times, though a fair proportion disappears through the exhaust ports during the scavenging process).

For the August re-appraisal the latest results from the single- and twin-cylinder unit testing by Ricardo was taken into consideration. Ricardo was getting 270 lb bmep and running at 3500 rpm on the shorter-stroke E.65. He was also forcing enough air into a cylinder to fill it 2.89 times. Farnborough then applied this information to a 12-cylinder main engine together with other improvements that were inevitable with time, such as supercharger efficiency. What they came up with was breathtaking. Top speed in MS gear at 14, 000 feet was approx 485 mph. In FS gear at 32,000 feet it was approximately 535 mph.

Looking at near approximations of the engines performance at these speeds we have,

	485 mph at 14,000 ft	535 mph at 32,000 ft
BMEP gross lb/sq.in	260	254
BHP gross	3660	3580
Air consumption lb/min	718	687
Supercharger horsepower	1310	2065
Propellor horsepower	2345	1530
Exhaust thrust lb F	919	1068
Jet thrust lb	656	860
Jet power converted to engine BHP	1130	1750
Net engine BHP (prop + jet)	3475	3280

All this on 26 litres!

These speeds are hardly surprising when it is realised that apart from the propellor's propulsive energy there was also jet thrust equivalent to half that being achieved from the best gas turbines at that time. Little wonder also that Farnborough considered the engine too powerful for the Spitfire airframe. Returning to reality the reader is reminded that these figures were for a hypothetical engine, though there is no reason to doubt their validity had the Crecy development continued along the lines of Farnborough's predictions.

In February 1943 Hives reported to the Ministry of Aircraft Production (MAP) that his Company was looking into the installation of the Crecy in the Mosquito. There were, however, "a large number of difficulties" making it impossible to take full advantage of the exhaust thrust. "We are still left that we have no suitable aeroplane for installing the 2-stroke engine to enable us to get the maximum performance".

If the Spitfire and Mosquito were unsuitable then the North American P-51 Mustang would have seemed the ideal airframe for the developed Crecy, in particular the lightweight F and G models which were half a ton lighter than the versions then in production. It must be considered a strong possibility that the above-configured Crecy, or the exhaust turbine version, would push the Mustang to around 600 mph at altitude; if, that is, propellor technology allowed it to. This was never proposed but something along these lines was attempted during the latter stages of the war.

Hucknall's experience with the Mustang in 1942, when it installed the two-stage Merlin in place of the Allison, initiated a study of fitting the Crecy into a design based mainly on this aircraft with its advanced aerodynamics. Initially conceived as a private venture fighter, with a Merlin or Griffon installed in the fuselage behind the pilot, its role changed to that of a flying test bed for various engine configurations. This is one example where the in-line, liquid-cooled engine scores over the air-cooled radial – ie, versatility in installation. With the small fuselage cross-section of a fighter a radial engine of any substantial power cannot be buried within a fuselage without incurring drag problems in the supply of cooling air.

Three schemes featured the Crecy, the first being a straight forward installation with the engine exhaust providing ejector thrust in the normal manner. Normal, that is except for its quantity, which produced over a third of the propulsion power at speed and altitude. The second scheme featured the exhaust-driven turbine whose energy was fed back into the crankshaft to relieve the energy that drove the propellor and supercharger, in other words a compound engine.

The ultimate scheme was most ingenious. This involved an exhaust-driven turbine, called a thrust augmentor, with an outer annulus that was fed with the air from the radiator/oil cooler. The resultant mixture exhausted into a jet pipe, combustion being assisted by the ignition of any unburnt fuel within the air purged through the exhaust ports during the scavenge cycle. The scheme could be likened to a primitive form of the bypass jet. Taking this idea a stage further there were hopes that if sufficient thrust could be generated then the propellor could be dispensed with, and one of the Miles M.46 proposals was schemed in such a manner. Shades of the Caproni-Campini CC.2 of 1940! Although work was well underway on the first aircraft, to be powered by a Griffon, the project was eventually abandoned by the war's end.

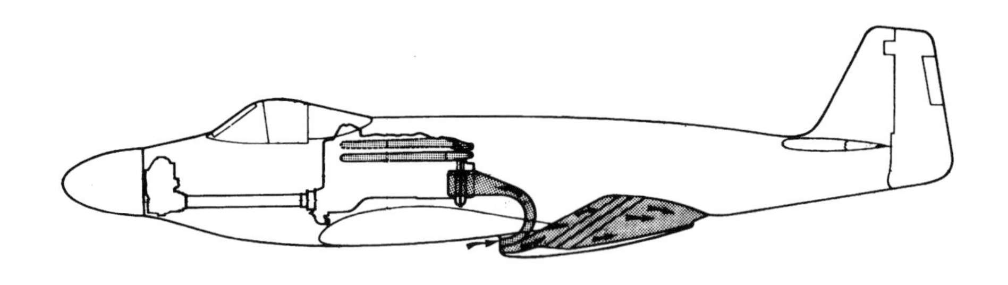

P. I. ENGINE WITH SIMPLE EJECTOR EXHAUST

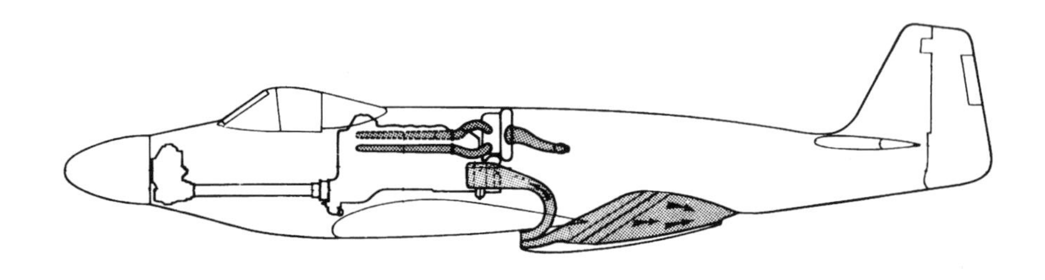

P. I. ENGINE WITH EXHAUST CRANKSHAFT-TURBINE AUGMENTER

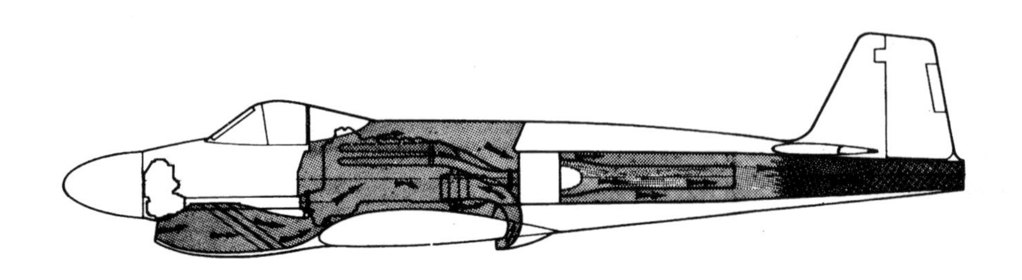

P. I. ENGINE WITH SEPARATE EXHAUST THRUST AUGMENTER

The three Crecy installations as proposed for Hucknall's Mustang-based Flying Test Bed. In the final scheme the weight of the thrust augmentor dictated the re-siting of the radiator to beneath the nose of the aircraft giving the airflow through it a simple straight-through run to the augmentor.

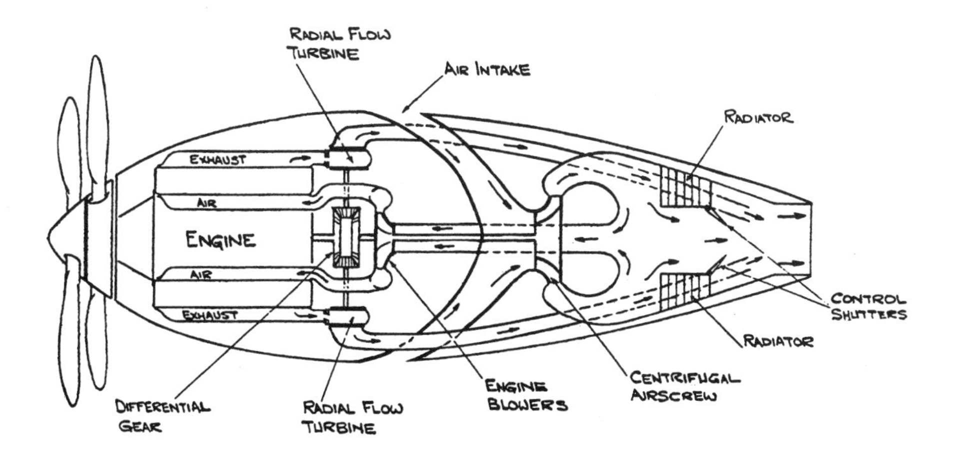

A scheme, dated 27 November 1944, showing another example of the Crecy as a compound engine. This plan view shows an engine with only one exhaust bank per cylinder block, each driving a turbine from which shafts protrude to drive a differential gear. Power from the turbine is fed back into the crankshaft and also to drive a shaft with a centrifugal compressor at each end. The forward compressor is the engine's supercharger supplying scavenge air to the cylinders. The rear compressor (referred to as a 'centrifugal airscrew' and acting as the first stage of the two-stage supercharging) draws in external air via intakes on either side of the nacelle. Some of this air is ejected rearwards, through controlling flaps to exhaust as jet thrust along with the turbine exhaust. It also provides the cooling medium for the dragless radiators within its stream. The forward compressor draws its air from this flow to feed the engine thus completing the cycle.

By the end of the war most problems concerning aero-engine installation were well understood if not actually overcome. This promoted a whole new science at Derby and Hucknall whereby new engines, whether built or still on paper, or even figments of the imagination , were schemed into advanced design installations. The Crecy with its unique attributes was tailor-made for the imaginative designer, some of whom spent all their time thinking years ahead, churning out drawings of installations featuring mythical engines of diverse capacities, cylinder numbers and configurations.

The abandonment of two-stroke development in early 1946 brought to a close the Crecy programme and Derby's interest in this class of engine. However, over at Hucknall there was a man who would not let sleeping dogs lie. His name was Stewart Tresilian (his middle name was Stewart, also), an engineer taking second wind with the Company in which, in the late 1920s – early 1930s, he had been involved with engine development, including the Schneider Trophy R engine, prior to going his own way before the war broke out. Frank Stark, who worked with him at Lagonda cars and became a close friend, said of him "In my opinion Tresilian was probably the best piston engine technician in Europe. At one time I would have said the world...." On his return to Rolls-Royce he found himself at Hucknall as one of a small team in the Design Project Department. He was extremely gifted when it came to engines and quickly realised the potential of the two-stroke principle. During the war, when he was a technical liaison man with the American Army Air Force he had designed or schemed an engine described as a 'liquid-cooled radial without an external radiator'. At Hucknall he was surrounded by the most experienced installation design and development team in the world.

He was well aware of Ricardo's work with two-strokes and studied with interest the Crecy development reports in the technical library. He saw nothing wrong with the basic mechanics of the engine but what he had in mind were dramatic changes in its size and operation. His studies culminated in a report issued in 1948, a report with never a dull moment.

Tresilian believed that small piston engines could be designed, without significant departure from the current practice, to better the propellor turbine easily on size, weight and fuel consumption. Where range was a criterion it could also afford considerable competition to the pure jet. He considered four-stroke and two-stroke, 16-cylinder, X-configuration designs and compared them with Griffon and Tweed powerplants. In both cases his designs were sized at 2500 bhp so as to make the comparison fair. The AP25 Tweed would have been, had it been built, an axial-flow propjet for post-war transport aircraft.

It was well known that in piston engines a reduction in cylinder size whilst maintaining the same bmep and piston speed increased the bhp per cubic inch of displacement. Scaling down an engine to half the cylinder capacity reduced the power by approximately 37%, which is the percentage reduction in piston area. The bhp per cubic inch of displacement increases by 25% due to the ability to run smaller engines faster and so displace their volume more often. He outlined a number of changes to a Griffon that would, one-by-one, bring down the size of the cylinders whilst still maintaining 2500 bhp.

The Griffon had a capacity of 36.7 litres, 340 sq.ins. of total piston area and piston speed of 3000 fpm. The result of applying the changes to that engine were as follows:

Use of triptane fuel; would enable reduction in piston area by 25% for same power with a corresponding reduction in valve area. This would reduce the capacity to 23.4 litres.

Change to 16 cylinders; this would produce reductions in engine weight and length and improve the crankshaft dynamically. For the same piston area but with a reduced stroke there is a further reduction to 20.3 litres.

Increase in piston speed; can be achieved considerably without big-end loading reaching that of a 9-cylinder radial engine, the only limitation being valve area. This can be increased by having valves the same size as the current seats seating in a steel head. Piston speed could then be increased by 33% and the total piston area further reduced by 25% and still maintain the same airflow and horsepower. The engine is now down to 13.2 litres.

Reduction of bore/stroke ratio; further increase in big-end loading is possible to equal that of the 9-cylinder radial allowing ratio to be reduced from 1.1 to .85.

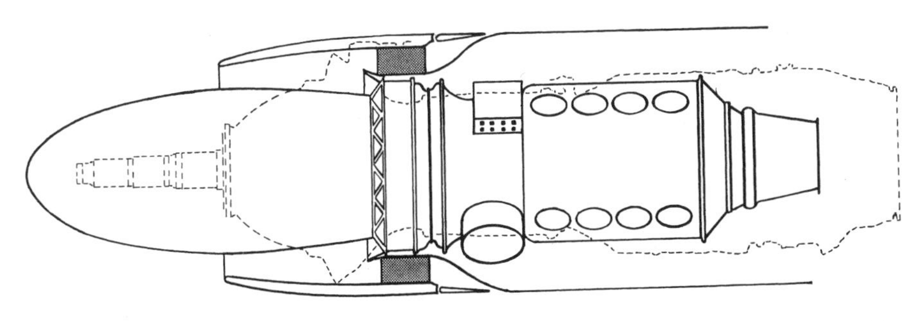

Tresilian's nine-litre, 2500 bhp, sixteen-cylinder, X- configuration, sleeve-valve, two-stroke engine. The widest part of the engine is the Griffon supercharger, 26 inches in diameter, behind which is the square-shaped injection pump unit and below, the magneto. Cylinder heads protrude through the annular exterior casing which direct exhaust into the turbo and out through a jet nozzle. The annular radiator matrix encircles the supercharger. The projected AP25 Tweed turboprop of the same power is shown in broken-line outline.

According to Tresilian, incorporation of the above changes would result in an engine with a 3.9-inches bore x 3.3-inches stroke, a piston area of 192 sq.ins, piston speed of 4000 fpm, an engine speed of 7250 rpm. Brake horsepower would be maintained at 2500 but the capacity would be down to 10.3 litres. The air mass flow would be the same as the Griffon, but due to extra boosting the total valve area would be only 75% of that of the Griffon. Cylinder block length would be about 45% of the Griffon and diameter of the engine about the same as the Griffon supercharger. BMEP would be 437 lb/sq.in.

In applying the above philosophy to the two-stroke engine it has to be remembered that it does not have poppet valves and that unlike the four-stroke, 25% of the air from the supercharger exits into the exhaust ports before they are closed by the sleeve.

Tresilian considered the Crecy's inlet port area unnecessarily large for 2500 bhp so this was reduced by 22% to 9 sq.ins. and the exhaust port area by 15%. At 25 lb boost this allowed an air intake of 6.75 lb/sec. In conjunction with this change the sleeve stroke was increased to 45% of the piston's stroke instead of 30% and the timing period extended slightly. The piston and sleeve strokes were then scaled down, the cylinder having the same effective port area as the Crecy but with a bore/stroke ratio of .75 instead of 1.3. This gave the sixteen cylinders a 3.9-inches bore x 2.9-inches stroke, 9 litres capacity, as opposed to the twelve-cylinder Crecy's 5.1 x 6.5 inches respectively for 26 litres. BMEP was 263 psi and brake horse power per litre an impressive 277.

The small cylinders would permit a compression ratio of 8:1 which, along with the 25% excess scavenge air and stratified charge, would give a tolerable exhaust temperature of 1100K to feed into the turbo. To attain the required 2500 bhp the engine would turn at 6800 rpm giving a piston speed of 3300 fpm. This would produce an inertia loading on the big-ends of around 5650 lb/sq.in, a somewhat high figure. However, because each stroke is a compression and firing stroke these forces are reduced considerably. At TDC the air in the cylinder compresses to about 600

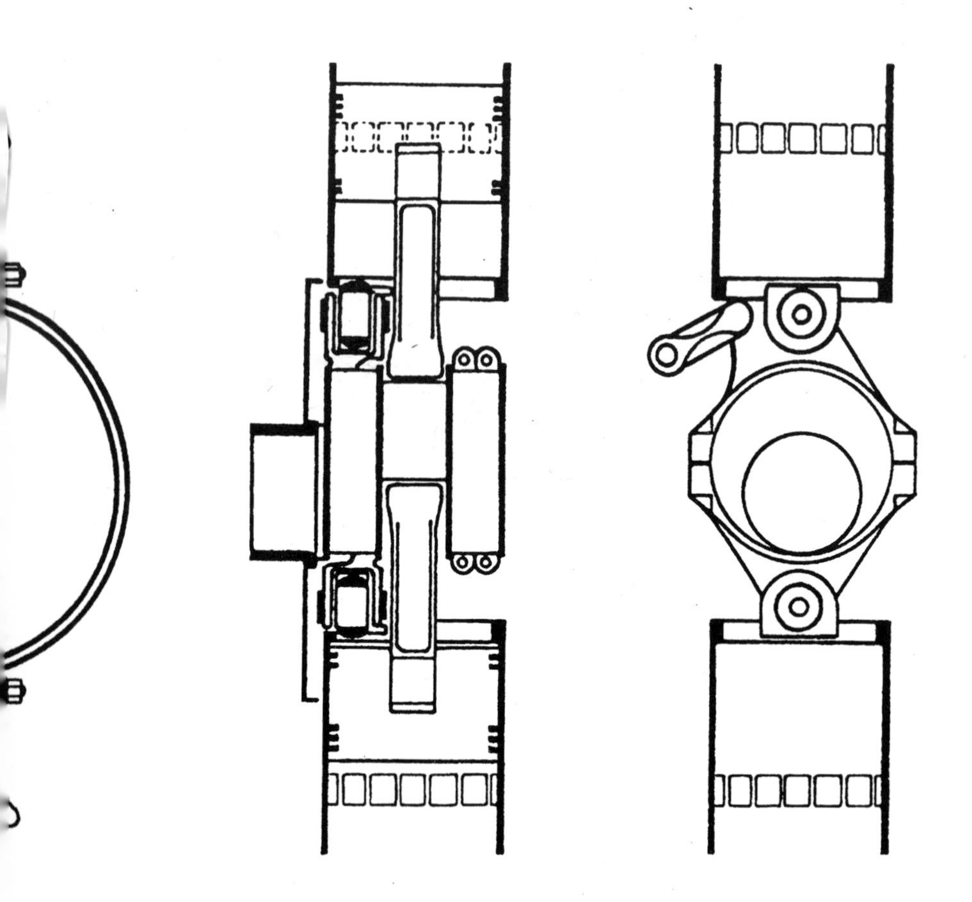

ir sleeves. The sleeve-drive mechanism is not shown in this view. Prominent are the double-skinned ducts, the
tre illustration shows the sleeve drive from the crankshaft eccentric. The right-hand drawing depicts a stepped
ther eccentric on the other side of the big-end.

Cross-section through Tresilian's engine showing the master con-rod and its three slaves driving the pistons within t
outer of which channels the exhaus t gases to the turbine, and the inner the scavenge air from the supercharger. The c
cross-section of the eccentric strap with two sleeves attached. The opposite pair (at 90-degrees) were driven from th

lb/sq.in but when partial combustion takes place this rises to 1000 lb/sq.in, reducing the big-end inertia pressure to about 2000 lb, not far from the normal V-12 practice. To avoid firing four cylinders together the two throws of each half of the crankshaft were positioned 45° from the plane of each other.

In appearance the engine would have been like no other, with the Griffon two-stage supercharger at the front (at 26 inches diameter it was the widest part of the engine) and the exhaust turbine at the rear giving the impression of a small jet engine. The two were interconnected by geared shafts running down the side of the engine. The entire surface of the engine itself was surrounded by a duct, save for the exposed cylinder heads. Actually, there were four ducts, each double skinned, which channelled the exhaust rearward to the turbine. No welding was employed in their construction. Beneath the ducts were the channels through which the air from the supercharger was fed into the inlet ports. The inlet channels did not exist as ducts like the exhaust but were formed by the lower skin of the exhaust duct and the outer surface of the engine crankcase.

The turbo would provide more power than that required for boosting, the excess taking some of the load off the crankshaft to the extent that fuel consumption would better the four-stroke by between 15 to 35% over the range of altitudes.

The resultant engine would be very light in weight but the problem still remained of absorbing 2500 bhp through a reduction gear and contra-rotating propellor set. Such items for an engine of this power would weigh around 700 lb – well over 50% of the engine-only weight. Tresilian was in favour of an American idea of multiple blades at high speed and proposed such a scheme employing single rotation at crankshaft speed, i.e. no reduction gearing. He saw a reduction in vibration levels, low torque reaction and a further saving in weight. As a powerplant complete with radiators, cowling, mounting and airscrew it would weigh 2150 lb. This represented a 43% saving over the equivalent four-stroke engine previously described and a 23% betterment over the turbine Tweed. Cruising fuel consumption at .37 lb/hp/hr was 26% better than the four-stroke, 36% better than the Tweed. A rough estimate was made of the range of the Douglas DC-4M airliner with four two-stroke engines installed instead of Merlins. It showed a range with full payload of 4750 miles instead of 3750.

By playing tunes with various bores, strokes, engine speeds, boost pressures and cylinder numbers the same power of 2500 bhp could be achieved for an engine diameter of only 23 inches and a further reduction in capacity to 7.8 litres. For those who liked to think big what better than an X-24-configured two-stroke engine with a Griffon bore and a 3.6-inches stroke, 4600 rpm and 35 lb boost to give 39 litres (2 litres more than the standard Griffon) and 8100 bhp. At this time the Avon produced an equivalent 8500 hp at 500 mph.

Alas, Tresilian's schemes came to nothing and have lain dormant ever since. Hives wanted him back at Derby working under Adrian Lombard on gas turbines but, though the two were not enemies, they didn't often see eye-to-eye with each other and Tresilian again left the Company, this time for good, and went on to join the BRM racing-car engine design team and do lots of other interesting things.

Other applications

In the final months of 1943 the Company was thinking about its post-war prospects, not only with regard to aero-engines but in all other aspects of transportation including land and sea. In all cases the petrol-injection or compression-ignition two-stroke was envisaged as the power plant. The applications ranged from 5000 hp aero-engines, for both civil and military use, through a range of powers suitable for such marine craft as small cargo/passenger ships and motor yachts; tanks, locomotives, lorries, cars and down to generating sets. In all cases the two-stroke was seen as the means of providing that which is always being sought after, namely, more power, reduced size, lighter weight, lower fuel consumption and cost.

At this time the common four-stroke petrol and diesel engines employed in commercial service vied with each other for superiority. Whilst the diesel had a slightly greater bhp per litre advantage, the petrol engine was 55% lighter in weight and there was no improv ement in this respect that could be applied to the former that could not be of similar advantage to the latter. The two-stroke, Rolls-Royce

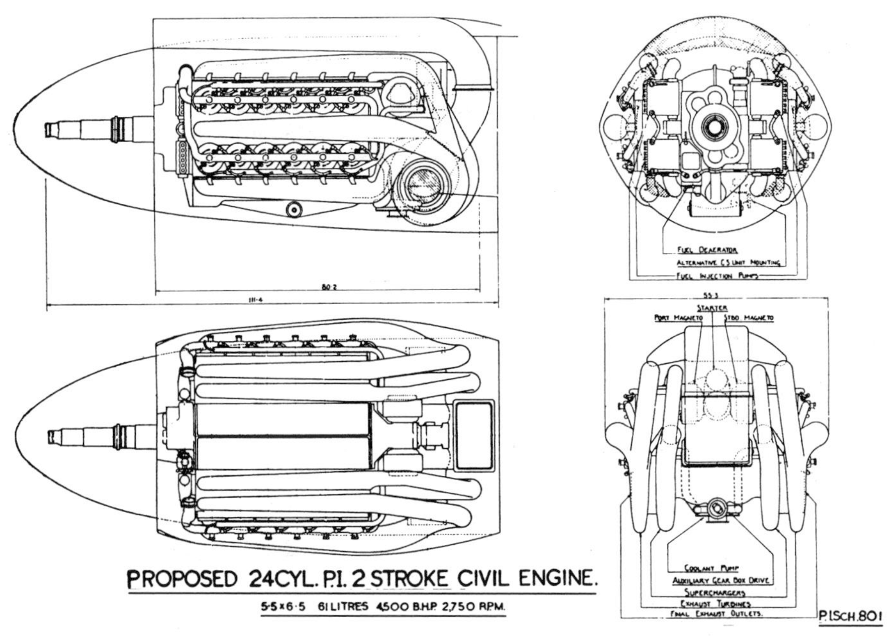

Had the turboprop not gained prominence so swiftly in the early post-war years, the requirements for a powerful transport engine might have been met by the two-stroke, petrol-injection principle. Should such a need have reached fruition then the powerplant might have looked something like the above example. The scheme depicts an H-24 layout in which the left and right cylinder blocks each feed their exhausts into a dedicated turbine. Each turbo drives its own supercharger into which air is drawn from a downdraught air intake. In this form the engine would develop 4500 bhp from its 61 litres at 2750 rpm. A military variant, with the air intake beneath the engine, would develop 5500 bhp at 3000 rpm.

reasoned, had a distinct advantage over both four-strokes in that whilst the function of both types of engine are the same with regard to inducting air, compressing it and adding fuel, and the resultant speeds, pressure and loads are the same per stroke, the two-stroke achieves its objectives within one revolution, not two. The four-stroke, as Stanley Hooker once said, has one stroke to produce the power and three to wear it out. Therefore, with each cylinder producing its power at each revolution of the engine, only half the number of cylinders are required to produce the equivalent power and torque of the four-stroke. Actually, this is not quite true because the ports of a two-stroke must be open for a greater portion of the stroke to scavenge and refill the cylinder.

The key element in this achievement was the disposal of the exhaust and the replenishment of air into the cylinder within part of one cycle. To do this efficiently some form of supercharging had to be employed but this would offset the advantages gained by re-introducing the weight saved by the reduction in cylinders, not to mention the loss in power output to drive the supercharger. By introducing an exhaust turbine coupled to the supercharger the lost power could be comfortably restored, but not, of course, the weight penalty. The turbine would also provide the means of improving the fuel consumption over the four-stroke for without it the two-stroke's superior power would be at the expense of a greater fuel burn. An exhaust turbine could, of course, improve the performance of a four-stroke engine but the higher exhaust temperatures would have precluded the use of cheaper blade materials made possible by the two-stroke's scavenge air mixing. Because of its sea-

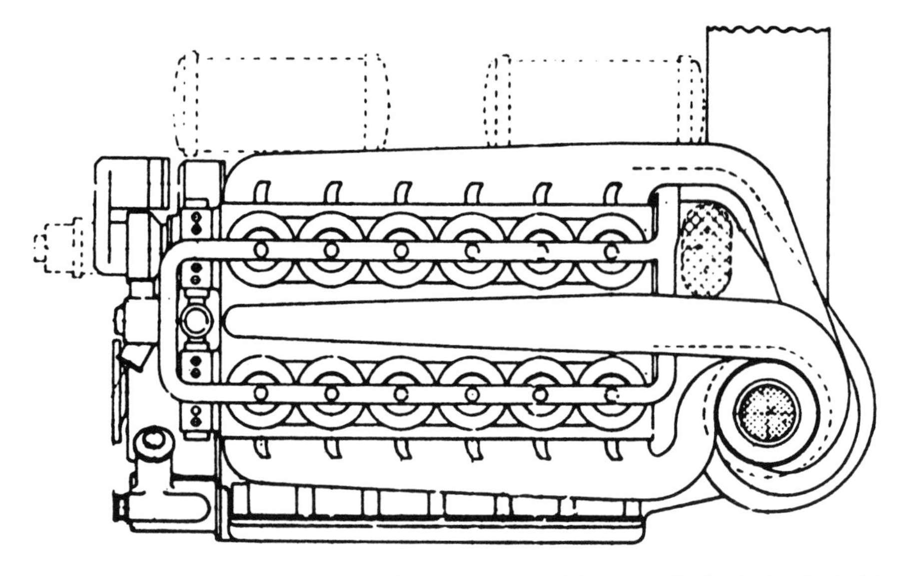

The H-24 configuration was also considered for marine use though for this application the diesel principle was preferred over petrol-injection. Such an engine would have a final-drive speed not exceeding 1250 rpm, giving 2400 bhp. The flanged drive shaft can be seen at left.

level operation the engine, unlike its aeronautical counterpart, would not be required to be highly developed in an effort to produce as much power as possible, indeed a supercharger compression ratio of only 1.75 was considered sufficient, as was a bmep of 85 lb. Such benign conditions would negate the need for exotic materials in favour of the more common, for example, steel fabrication for the crankcase and cast iron for the pistons.

Not one of the proposed engines ever got any further than the drawing board. The only innovation that reached fruition was, as we have already seen, the exhaust turbine, finally mated to the Crecy before the axe fell on the project. It must be assumed that the development problems experienced with the Crecy, still years away from resolution in 1946, stifled any post-war ideas of introducing two-stroke sleeve-valve engines into the established forms of land, sea, air and rail transport, not to mention power generation. It is, perhaps, interesting to note that when Rolls-Royce finally formed an Oil Engine Division in the late 1940s its designs were founded on well-established Diesel principles. In the 1960s, when the Division had moved to Crewe, it produced its K range which were opposed-piston, two-stroke supercharged diesel engines.

EPILOGUE

The Crecy started as a compression-ignition diesel engine. When the conversion to petrol with spark-ignition was proposed by the Air Ministry, Hives was at first reluctant and did not agree until the outbreak of hostilities. His reluctance indicated doubt whether the then PI could be an influence in the conflict and this doubt stayed with him, and rightly so.

When the Crecy was being developed the outcome of the war was in the balance. The improvements and uprating of the Merlin, which was in front-line action every day, were the top priority. Hives above all was aware of this and was not about to divert the teams working on the Merlin, Griffon or Vulture to work on the Crecy which could not become a factor in the struggle for several years, regardless of the success of its development.

The embryo of the Two-stroke Division was being manned in 1938 when Rolls-Royce were involved in the military build-up. Harry Wood was not permitted to recruit from the staff engaged on other aircraft engines to avoid weakening their efforts. All the technical personnel were recent hires from outside the Company or transfers from the car side. The personnel engaged in the design and development of the CI, which became the PI and then the Crecy, were functionally separated from personnel engaged on the other engine programmes. The programme used the test facilities of the various specialised groups, such as supercharger, mechanical components and electrical but the involvement of their engineers was minimised.

The thermodynamic performance of the two-stroke cylinder assembly had been developed by Ricardo and was not improved in Derby. Ricardo had also developed the mechanical capability of the piston, cylinder and sleeve assembly at the Kestrel size of the E.65 engine. What the engine needed was good mechanical skills, experience and intuition to scale up the cylinder dimensions and make a 12-cylinder engine. Under the restrictions placed on him Wood was not able to recruit staff with the necessary qualities.

Hives realised the problem when he transferred responsibility for Crecy development to Lovesey. This did not work out because the latter could not spare the time to think through the problems and come up with solutions and because the Crecy was detracting from his other higher-priority responsibilities. During the period while Lovesey was responsible for the Crecy the quality of the reports of test runs and the development efforts reflected an improvement over the reports and corrective measures under Wood. When the Crecy was returned to Wood, Spike Corbitt was made responsible for development. Spike was an aerodynamics and performance guru at heart. These were not the skills required to straighten out the Crecy. Detail mechanical engineering was the requirement.

As Crecy development dragged on, Hives would have known that it could not to be developed in time to influence the outcome of hostilities; his interest in the development was probably as a transport engine for when peace returned. When it became apparent that the future was in the gas turbine the decision to discontinue the Crecy was the correct one.

The disappointing outcome of the Crecy programme can be blamed more on the pressures of wartime which prevented the assignment of qualified talent to the project rather than to a weakness in the concept of the engine. A mechanical genius such as Lovesey, Cantrill, Harvey-Bailey or Hives might well have licked the Crecy into shape and produced an outstanding engine. This was prevented by the advent of the jet engine which was the ultimate knockout blow for all large piston aero engines. In view of the difficulties which attended the birth of the practical gas turbine during the war, the rapidity of its subsequent development may, with hindsight, seem remarkable, and it surprised many contemporary observers in the industry.

The high fuel consumption of the early gas turbine seemed to reserve it particularly for combat aircraft, and a substantial body of opinion maintained that a major role would remain for the conventional piston engine in civil and in long-range military applications. There were also those who believed that an intermediate compound form, combining the virtues of both the gas turbine and the reciprocating engine would prove to be the best solution for general air transport. Perhaps the most extreme example of this line of thought was the Nomad, Napier's 12-cylinder, two-stroke, compounded diesel turbine – an engine which achieved unparalled fuel economy, but no sales.

In fact, the really successful intermediate between piston engines and jet power for transport aircraft proved to be the propellor-turbine – the form in which Dr A A Griffith had first envisaged harnessing the gas turbine power for propulsion in 1926.

Rolls-Royce, however, was extremely resolute in its commitment to the new powerplant (perhaps through having played such a major part in bringing it into practical operation), and the paper the Company communicated to the Aeronautical Research Council in January 1946 both rang the death knell for the Crecy project and put the case for a full commitment to the continued development of the turbine engine.

AERONAUTICAL RESEARCH COUNCIL

Crecy Two-Stroke Engine
By
Rolls-Royce Ltd

14th January, 1946

It has always been the Rolls-Royce policy to place the whole of their technical facilities at the disposal of the Air Ministry for the purpose of maintaining the superiority of the Royal Air Force. In pursuance of this policy we have undertaken the basic development of practically every type of aircraft power unit, including liquid-and air-cooled, four-stroke engines, two-stroke engines with turbine combinations and a variety of complete turbine engine projects.

At the commencement of these projects each had its own particular merit, but during the process of development some were bound to go ahead of others as the general picture became more clear and the degree of merit established.

As a result of this work we are convinced that the turbine engine will eventually replace reciprocating types for aircraft, and it is just a question of how long the time will be and what engines will be used during that period. The advantages already established with the turbine engine on the score of weight, power output, reliability, simplified installation, reduced maintenance and fire risk, cannot be achieved on any types of reciprocating engines and we believe there are potential possibilities of competing favourably in fuel consumptions.

To accomplish this in the shortest possible time we feel we must concentrate more effort on the more promising projects. Our capacity for design, development and experimental manufacture has been so far distributed between the various projects, and the increased effort needed on turbine work can only be made at the expense of dropping one or more of the reciprocating parts. After giving the matter a considerable amount of thought, we have decided to recommend the dropping of the two-stroke engine development for the following reasons:-

(1) There are no aeroplane commitments for this type of power unit as is the case with the four-stroke engine projects, nor are we sufficiently far advanced with the development to approach aircraft designers.

(2) For the two-stroke engine to compete with the four-stroke it must function in conjunction with a turbine; it then has the merit of developing higher maximum powers on 100 octane fuel for a given piston displacement, maintaining a low fuel consumption up to 90 per cent of its maximum power.

    The Crecy has actually demonstrated the possibility of surpassing the four-stroke in power, consumption at maximum power and heat rejected to coolant. Its principal virtue of furnishing low consumptions at high cruising powers, however, cannot be made use of since the operational requirements for long-range aircraft call for 25 – 50 per cent of maximum take-off power. At this reduced cruising power the four-stroke engine is actually superior on specific fuel consumption.

    As regards operational characteristics, the two-stroke is in the turbine engine class in that it is a full-throttle engine and functions most economically at the high cruising powers. It has not, however, the advantages possessed by the turbine engine as regards weight and power for size, necessity for cooling systems, freedom from installational complications of the combined engine and turbine, and from vibration due to reciprocating parts.

(3) In making these recommendations we are conscious of the fact that we shall be throwing away a good deal of valuable accumulated experience gained during the development of the two-stroke as an aero engine. For this reason we have also given careful consideration to the future possibilities of using it solely as a means of supplying hot gas under pressure to operate a power turbine. For this application the power developed by the two-stroke is absorbed in compressing air to which heat is added during the combustion and mixing process in the engine before delivery to the turbine nozzles.

    The main advantage of this scheme lies in the possible low fuel consumption obtained by driving the compressor in this manner. When operating on the diesel cycle where a high compression ratio can be employed, it should be possible to obtain a consumption figure of 0.38 lb/bhp/hr, and maybe a little lower, depending upon the engine performance, charging efficiency, and exit temperatures of the gases, with the reduced fire risk of the heavy fuel.

The weight and size of such an engine, however, would be very much greater than that of the turbine and its combustion equipment to do the same work. The relatively low engine rpm will necessitate a step-up gear to drive the compressor, and there will be the same power plant weight disadvantages and complication by having to provide radiators and oil coolers. The vibration problems will still be present, and there is no reason to suppose that the two-stroke engine operating under the high power conditions w ill be any more reliable than existing four-strokes.

Our investigations into the optimum performance to be obtained by the compounding of turbine engines, indicate the possibility of eventually attaining fuel consumptions of the order of 0.4 lb/bhp/hr without the use of heat exchangers. At the lower cruising powers, however, the specific consumption tends to increase rapidly due to the loss of compression ratio with rpm, but this could be mitigated to a large extent by designing the size of unit for the desired cruising power and utilising a combination of afterburning and water injection for take-off and emergency power in flight.

In multi-engined aircraft optimum specific consumptions can be obtained when cruising at 50 per cent maximum power by stopping a number of the engines in flight. Projected designs already provide for this by grouping propeller turbine engines in pairs, each operating one set of blades on a contra-rotating airscrew.

(4) Projected aircraft designs using turbine engine power plants predominate over any other type because of the general improvement obtained in performance. We are, therefore, definitely committed to a number of types of turbine engines which will require all the possible effort to produce them in the time available.

(5) There are relatively few types of aircraft projected for special long-range operation or extreme hours of endurance. Since the power units for these projects must be capable of operating at the low percentage of maximum power at the lowest possible specific fuel consumption, the requirements can only be met by the reciprocating types.

Comparing the performance of the Crecy with the Merlin for this particular duty, there appears little to choose between the two, the advantage being on the side of the Merlin when fitted with a turbine. This is indicated by the following figures:-

Two-stroke plus turbine

Operating 90 per cent maximum power – fuel consumption
0.37 lb/bhp/hr

Operating 25 per cent maximum power – fuel consumption
0.42 lb/bhp/hr

Merlin 24 with 7:1 compression ratio pistons plus turbine

0.37 lb/bhp/hr at optimum cruising power rising slightly as the power is increased or decreased.

A Merlin 24 engine fitted with 7:1 compression pistons without the turbine, is projected for special long-range 'Lincolnian' aircraft which will have an estimated range of 10,000 miles or 55 hours duration, using a mixture of Methanol and water injection for take-off.

The actual figures obtained on the test bed furnish consumptions of 0.41 to 0.425 lb/bhp at 10,000 ft. over a range of powers varying from 350 to 1,000. Fitting a turbine to this engine and either gearing back into the crankshaft or driving a separate airscrew, furnishes the estimated consumption figures of 0.36 to 0.37 lb/bhp/hr.

General remarks

Had the Crecy power unit reached the stage of proved reliability, its improved performance over the conventional four-stroke might have filled the gap whilst the turbine engine was being fully developed. A good deal of mechanical development however remains to be done on this unit, and with the limited effort we can afford to concentrate on it, we are convinced a better turbine engine will be in production before the two-stoke combination.

The problems met during the development of the Crecy ruled out the possibilities of its being in production in time to contribute to the war effort, and owing to the enormous war demands made for the development of our conventional four-stroke types for the R.A.F. , the work had to proceed on a lower category of priority. Taking all these factors into account, and since we have considerable experience in turbine technique, we feel it would be a mis-direction of effort for us to continue further with any two-stroke development.

* * * * *

Although little has been published about the Crecy, Sir Harry Ricardo, in his book *'The High Speed Internal Combustion Engine'* wrote extensively about his two-cycle, open-ended-sleeve- configuration engines, and there have been other reports of this concept. The configuration is recognised as most promising for high output reciprocating engines with possibly the potential for the highest specific output of any system.

The role of the reciprocating engine may be over for large aircraft but there are signs of a resurgence of interest in the two-cycle engine for vehicle and marine propulsion. This renewal of interest is favoured by the availability of electronic ignition and fuel injection which solve the problems with high-speed ignition and injection previously inherent in two-cycle engines.

In the USA there have been several programmes for engines requiring high power and good fuel efficiency which have used the Ricardo confi guration. They have not come to fruition because the need for the intended application ended. At the time of writing, the Ricardo two-stroke configuration is under consideration as a replacement for Merlin engines in racing aircraft and racing power boats. It might be hoped that this narrative will help to further the development of two-stroke engines.

Crecy reminiscences and comments

by Geoff Wilde

Over the years 1940 to 1943 I was responsible for experimental and development work on all of the centrifugal superchargers. These included Peregrine, Merlin, Vulture, Griffon, Exe, PI (later named Crecy) and the Eagle. The Merlin supercharger work, of course, received the lion's share of the effort. For this work I reported to Stanley Hooker who at that time was Chief Assistant to A C Lovesey the Chief Experimental Engineer. He succeeded Jimmy Ellor when he and Colonel Barrington, Chief Designer, were transferred to the Packard Company in Detroit to oversee the manufacture and development of the Packard Merlin engines.

During 1940/44 very little information seemed to leak out from the PI engine development team. There had been twin-cylinder engines on the single-cylinder testbeds at Nightingale Road, but it was not until the complete twelve-cylinder engine was run at Sinfin, producing a characteristic deafening high-pitched sound, that everyone became aware that something unusual was happening.

The Chief Development Engineer of the PI development team was Richard Thomas, who was often seen walking in a carefree manner in his plus-fours between the PI development office and the single-cylinder testbeds. I once asked him how the engine was performing and what power was being produced. The answer he gave was "the engine will give more power than the Merlin and even if made of cast-iron will have a higher power-to-weight ratio than the Merlin". One could not take him seriously.

'Spike' Corbitt, who had been Rowledge's technical assistant on the Exe engine, had been transferred to the PI development team. Spike was the most highly qualified member of the team (MSc and Whitworth Senior Scholar). He was inventive but somewhat of an eccentric who did not communicate in a rational manner. Spike and Thomas did not see eye to eye. That did not help.

Sometime in 1942 I first became directly involved with PI development work. It was being said that the supercharger was not giving sufficient pressure on the engine. What could we do about it? It was then that I was introduced for the first time to the engine sleeve-valve timing changes that were being made to investigate the effect on piston temperature of altering a factor called the 'boost swept volume', or BSV. This was the ratio of the air that passed through the cylinder to the air that burned with the injected fuel. The trend had been to increase the BSV factor from 1.2 to as high as 1.6. During engine mechanical development this seemed often to be changed to assess the effect on piston temperature, and every time it was changed the flow matching point on the supercharger charactistics changed. At the higher BSV values the working point fell down the pressure ratio flow characteristic of the supercharger and the engine boost pressure fell. This was corrected at first by increasing the throat area of the supercharger diffuser vanes by 15%. I remember that we made several different diffusers to match the BSV values tested.

During late 1942 it was evident that the development of the PI engine was lagging behind expectations. The optimism and extravagant claims of superiority of performance made by the PI development team were not being realised. Hives became impatient. He directed that the PI engine should be transferred from Wood to Lovesey and Hooker for some three months for an overall assessment of the engine's potential to be made.

The stumbling block was inadequate piston cooling. This was no surprise to anyone because if you try to produce a given power from a piston and cylinder twice as often as in a four-stroke engine it is hardly surprising to find that the piston gets hotter! In a four-stroke engine the piston has time to cool on the exhaust and induction strokes, but in the PI two-stroke why should not high BSVs provide adequate cooling for the piston? A factor in this is the breathing capacity of the sleeve-valve ports. High BSVs will cause pressure losses and loss of power output unless the sleeve-valve ports have better flow coefficient and greater area than the poppet valves of the four-stroke engine in relation to piston area.

Hooker asked me to set up a simple flow test of the PI cylinder inlet ports and a similar test of the two inlet poppet valves of a Merlin, both in the fully open position. The flow coefficient of the sleeve valve ports was found to be no greater than that of the poppet valves. This seemed to be a surprise and a disappointment to everyone. It was not, of course, the only factor, the others being the ratio of the total sleeve valve port area to piston area, the period over which the ports are open, and the pressure drop across the ports.

In addition to this experimental work some theoretical work was undertaken by Hooker and Reed, chief of the performance office, to try to calculate the airflow through the PI engine cylinders along the lines that had been done successfully for the Merlin engine in 1940/41. A report was eventually issued on this work but by early 1943 the writing was already on the wall as regards the performance indications of the PI engine, as will be appreciated in the following.

At 2600 crank rpm and 18 lb/sq.in boost on the testbed, PI engine No.6 gave 1460 bhp with an airflow of 426 lb/min, or 3.4 bhp/lb/min airflow rate. By comparison the Merlin gave around 8 bhp/lb/min airflow rate. These PI figures are taken from a report published much later by the Supercharger Office. The report also gives the PI single-stage supercharger characteristics, the flow matching between the engine and supercharger, and the engine airflow formula that had been derived by Reed.

This dramatic difference between the bhp output per unit airflow of the PI engine and the Merlin sealed its fate. Lovesey and Hooker produced a report for Hives that recommended termination of PI engine development. [This report has not been found – Editor]

The low power output of the PI engine per unit airflow rate was due to two factors: wasted energy of the excess BSV air to cool the piston, and the effective volume compression ratio of the cylinder being much lower than the geometrical figure quoted (6.5:1). The effective ratio must take port opening and closing into account.

There are two things that rarely appear in the analysis of two-cycle engines; the thermal expansion ratio within the cylinder, which relates to the thermal efficiency of the power produced by the pistons; and the pressure losses between the engine exhaust port and the turbine. I do not believe these two factors are very well understood and with all due respect to the brains working on the Crecy I do not think that they understood them very well either. Just as the brilliant Wankel engine was struggling against an excess of cylinder surface area for efficient operation, so it seems to me that the Crecy was struggling against limited expansion ratio and a high pressure loss between exhaust port and turbine. The fact that the engine produced so much noise was another factor that suggested that when the exhaust valve opened the pressure within the cylinder was much higher than on the Merlin. Doubling the frequency of firing and reducing the expansion ratio is not the way to improve thermal efficiency.

Was the engine a misconception? As late as December 1942/January 1943 I was asked by Wood to make proposals for a two-stage centrifugal supercharger for the PI engine to increase boost pressure at high altitude (30,000 ft). This was to be in two alternative configurations. The first was to be similar to the Merlin two-stage supercharger, and the second was to have a smaller diameter double-sided first stage (following R engine practice) followed by a conventional second stage. The reason for the request was not made clear to me at the time. I responded to the request by giving performance and dimensional data.

Sensing that the end of PI development was approaching Wood and the PI development team became desperate. They wanted to go ahead with means of recovering the wasted exhaust energy of the excess BSV air through an exhaust turbine to drive the supercharger directly and eliminating the mechanical drive. The reason for the double-sided first stage of the second proposed two-stage supercharger was to enable the rotational speed of the supercharger to be increased to assist the power output capability of the driving exhaust turbine.

I think Spike was behind these schemes. The two-stage supercharger was never built, but a double-sided, single-stage centrifugal supercharger was designed, built and run on the supercharger rig at Nightingale Road during the last year of the project.

In summary, I am bound to think that the PI engine project was a misconception. That there are fashions in engineering cannot be denied. When your competitor makes a success of something there will always be those who want to follow. I think the fact that the Bristol engine company had made a success of developing the series of air-cooled radial engines with sleeve-valves was a factor in this. But the capability of those engines to produce high power output with high degrees of supercharge fell far short of the liquid-cooled engine with sodium-cooled exhaust valves. If the Merlin had had sleeve-valves we would most likely not have won the last war in the air. I am sure that Rowledge had a powerful influence on engine design policy at Rolls-Royce in the 1930s following the Schneider Trophy in stressing the superiority of the V-12 liquid-cooled engine with mechanically-driven supercharger. It was indeed fortunate for us all that development concentrated on this configuration of engine and installed powerplant in which as much as 150 propulsion horsepower was obtained in the Spitfire by direct jet reaction from the engine exhaust nozzles.

Apart from the fundamental power limitations of the PI engine, it came too late to be seriously considered for installation in any aircraft. It has been claimed that had jet propulsion not arrived, the PI engine would have been the next engine to follow the Merlin . I cannot see any substantial evidence for this view. The fact that the final and largest Rolls-Royce piston engine, the 3600 hp Eagle, had sleeve-valves is to me a remarkable fact when there is so little fundamental data available in favour of sleeve-valve performance. It shows the powerful influence of fashion and competition.

* * * * *

To this day argument abounds as to whether the two-stroke sleeve-valve engine would ever have proved its worth, let alone replaced the conventional four-stroke, and been the ideal interim prime-mover until the gas turbine became fully accepted.

The above recollection by Geoff Wilde would seem to infer that promises would not have been fulfilled. Dick Foster-Pegg would, however, disagree, basing his claim on the high performances and reliability achieved by the Ricardo single-cylinder units and not the state of development reached by Rolls-Royce.

Perhaps there is hope for it yet. The Ricardo company hasn't dismissed its principles completely and has proposed modern versions of engines for helicopter and high-altitude, long-duration applications.

APPENDIX I

This Appendix is a collection of extracts from some of the reports that still survive on the Crecy and whilst it repeats some of what has already been said it is felt that the reader's understanding would profit by their reproduction in this form more than by feeding their content piecemeal into the main text. There is also some good comparative detail with the Merlin. The reports are presented in chronological order commencing with some advanced thoughts from Spike Corbitt about post-Crecy two-stroke design – four months before the engine had commenced running!

Rg/Cbt.6/RS.23.12.40

Twin-cylinder firing on 12-cylinder 2-stroke engine

The idea of firing cylinders in pairs on the 2-stroke engine was proposed by the writer a year ago and although there were several points of merit in the scheme they were not sufficient to warrant its adoption at the time with the limited capacity of the 2-Stroke Section.

In the meantime further advantages have become apparent and original advantages confirmed, while some of the disadvantages now appear less important.

The idea is to use a symmetrical crankshaft as on the Merlin engine and fire cylinders equidistant from the centre main bearing together. The primary object was to obtain a crankshaft which would remain in balance over a long running period despite carbon formation on the pistons and sludge deposition in the crankpins.

With a symmetrical crankshaft two forms of engine are possible, a 60°-vee and a 180°-opposed engine. Which of these is used will depend on the installation possibilities though the 180°-opposed has easier bearing loads and exhaust pipes.

To avoid confusion the comparison with the present 90°-vee engine will be limited to the 60°-vee form.

The chief apparent disadvantages with the twin-cylinder firing were:-

(a) The torque variation becomes greater as it is equivalent to a 12-cylinder 4-stroke instead of a 24-cylinder 4-stroke engine.
This might mean a stronger crankshaft and gears.

(b) The centre main bearing load is very high as four cylinders adjacent to it are fired within 60°.

(c) The exhaust pipes inside the 60°-vee would be difficult.

These disadvantages are, however, not so serious. When the torsional vibration characteristics were examined it was found that there was only one forcing torque, the 6th order single node and this characteristic far outweighs the disadvantage of a more uneven basic torque.

The exhaust system becomes simpler, for to prevent pressure waves overlapping, the exhaust ports are divided up into groups of 3 requiring 8 exhaust pipes on the present engine.

The twin-cylinder firing reduces this to 4 main pipes and it should be no more difficult to get 2 pipes into a 60°-vee than 4 pipes into a 90°-vee.

The centre main bearing loading is not a real problem; it may be lengthened an inch if necessary without increasing engine weight as balance weights are removed from the crankshaft. The crankcase bending moment is not expected to give any trouble.

The advantages may be summed up as:-

(1) Crankshaft is easier to manufacture and balance and will not get out of balance with prolonged running.

(2) It should be possible to use a more efficient airscrew owing to the torsional characteristics.

(3) The vee angle is closed to 60° making a neater installation.

(4) Bulk and weight are saved on the following items:-

   (a) Exhaust pipes – only 4 main pipes are required instead of 8.

   (b) Lanchester balancers required by the eccentric drive may be deleted.

   (c) The crankshaft balance weights are not required.

It is recommended that the twin-firing system be used on any future 2-stroke engine.

It appears to have been proved on the Sabre as regards torsional characteristics and may be used on the Vulture. The 24-cylinder 4-stroke engine has at least 512 possible firing orders so that torsional troubles may be dodged to a certain extent without resorting to twin-cylinder firing, but a 2-stroke engine can have only one firing order so that there is no alternative once the engine is built.

* * * * *

Royal Aircraft Establishment
Report No. E.3932
March 1942

Estimated performance of a Spitfire
(Rolls-Royce two-stroke engine)
by
A W Morley and C Fougère

The net power available from the Rolls-Royce two-stroke engine has been estimated. The speeds it would give to a Spitfire have been calculated with and without allowance for exhaust thrust.

Case I: Engine with single-stage supercharger.

Case II: Engine with two-stage supercharger.

The engine characteristics have been used to estimate the effect on performance of installing it in a standard Spitfire in place of the present Merlin. With the single-stage version the rated height of 14,200 feet (static) becomes 20,000 feet when the additional ram from the air-intake at top speed is included; with the two-stage engine the top speed occurs at 35,000 feet.

Since the exhaust thrust plays a very important part in determining the top speed performance, it has been estimated with some care. The method relies essentially on the fact that the exhaust from the two-stroke engine will issue as a fairly steady stream from a collector manifold, and that the back pressure is a desired amount which must be maintained to control the airflow.

To demonstrate the importance of the exhaust thrust, the top speed of the Spitfire has been estimated both with and without this component. For comparison with a conventional engine, the performance of the Spitfire with a Griffon engine estimated in a similar manner is included. The Griffon engine is supposed fitted with a single-stage supercharger with the same compression ratio as assumed for the single-stage two-stroke engine so that the rated heights as well as top speeds may be compared.

The results compared the two-stroke with the Griffon and illustrate two important characteristics of the two-stroke engine. Firstly, the additional air pressure used to scavenge the two-stroke reduces its supercharger height. An efficient single-stage supercharger , with compression ratio 3.1:1, would give the two-stroke a rated height of 20,000 feet, compared with 23,000 feet for the Griffon. The extra 3000 feet in the latter case is equivalent to some 15 mph increase in the top speed of the Spitfire.

As a result of this, if exhaust thrust is neglected, the top speed of the Spitfire with the two-stroke engine is only 9 mph greater than that of the Griffon version in spite of the additional 250 bhp it develops.

The second point to be noted is the extreme importance of exhaust thrust on the two-stroke engine. The total thrust obtainable adds 48 mph to the top speed at 20,000 feet (403 to 451 mph) compared with 19 mph for the Griffon engine (394 to 413 mph). At higher altitudes its importance is still more marked; for example, the top speed of a two-stage supercharger version of the two-stroke, with a rated height of 35,000 feet, is increased from 420 to 486 mph by the exhaust thrust. In fact the advantage in performance of the two -stroke over a conventional four-stroke engine apparently depends completely on successful utilisation of this portion of the exhaust energy.

The exact fraction of full thrust to be expected in the case of the two-stroke will depend upon the flame-damping characteristics of the engine; very frequently, on engines at present in service, almost the whole of the exhaust thrust has been sacrificed to reduce the visibility of the exhaust at night. It is difficult to decide whether the two-stroke engine will require similar drastic measures; the excess scavenge air may be sufficient to cool the exhaust gas below the minimum temperature required for combustion, but on the other hand it may result in serious after-burning.

* * * * *

Addendum to Report No. E.3932. August 1942

At the request of the ARC Engine Sub-Committee, some preliminary calculations of the top speed of a Spitfire with the Rolls-Royce 2- stroke engine given in RAE report No. E.3932 have been extended, with certain modifications. In the original report, comparison was made with a Griffon II engine in a Spitfire at the altitudes of maximum power; this time the 2-stroke has been compared with the Griffon 61 over a range of altitudes. The Griffon 61 was chosen as it seemed a more serious competitor for the 2-stroke engine.

For the purpose of this investigation, the rated heights of the 2-stroke engine were adjusted so that with due allowance for intake ram and exhaust thrust the maximum power altitudes of the two engines would be the same. Engine conditions were 200 lb/sq.in gross bmep and 2750 rpm. Since the 200 lb/sq.in gross bmep for the 2-stroke is considered a low estimate, results are also given for the es timated bhp of this engine, at the same maximum power altitudes, assuming operation at the maximum conditions so far reached on test by Ricardo, viz. 270 lb/sq.in gross bmep, 3500 rpm, and 2.89 swept volumes air consumption. At this enhanced rating, the 2-stroke engine is much too powerful for the present Spitfire airframe.

From the results it was seen that there is little difference in the top speeds of the 2-stroke and Griffon 61 Spitfires at some altitudes – at 23,000 feet, the speeds are 403 mph and 399 mph respectively. At the higher altitudes the 2-stroke gains by reason of its extra exhaust thrust and at 40,000 feet, its top speed is 460 mph while that of the Griffon 61 is 424 mph.

It must be remembered when comparing the relative merits of the two engines that the Griffon 61 is much nearer production than the 2 -stroke. On the other hand, a gross 200 lb/sq.in bmep for the 2-stroke is well within this engine's capabilities, and it is possible that this figure will be greatly increased at a later date, and still higher speeds will be obtained.

As a rough indication of the speeds a Spitfire would reach with the 2-stroke operating at these higher powers, an estimate shows that velocities of approximately 484 mph at 14,000 feet and 535 mph at 32,000 feet would be attained.

* * * * *

ENGINE SUB-COMMITTEE
AERONAUTICAL RESEARCH COMMITTEE

MINUTES

The one-hundred and thirty-fifth meeting of the Engine Sub-Committee held at the Royal Aeronautical Society, 4 Hamilton Place, Piccadilly, London W1 on Tuesday, 22nd September, 1942, at 11.00am.

Present:- Sir H T Tizard (Chairman), Prof L Bairstow, Mr H Constant, Prof A C Egerton, Major F M Green, Cdr C M Hall, Mr H R Ricardo, Mr J L Naylor

(Secretary, ARC) and Mr A F C Brown (Secretary), Mr H Wood and Mr R W Corbitt of Messrs Rolls-Royce, Wing Cdr Whittle, Mr C O B Beal of Messrs Ricardo & Co, Dr H Roxbee Cox and Dr H Moss of the Ministry of Aircraft Production, Mr A W Morley and Mr W G A Perring of the Royal Aircraft Establishment and Mr W J Robinson of the Admiralty Engineering Laboratory.

Comparative Performance between Aircraft Powered by Two-Stroke or Jet Thrust Engines

6102 The estimated performance of a 'Spitfire' (Rolls-Royce two-stroke engine) – A W Morley and C M Fougère. Addendum to RAE Rep ort No. E.3932 (Secret).

6103 Comparison of fighter designs utilising the Rolls-Royce two-stroke engine or a jet propulsion unit – R Smelt and A W Morley. RAE Report No. E.3957.

THE CHAIRMAN explained that the Royal Aircraft Establishment had been asked to compare the relative merits of the Rolls-Royce two-stroke engine and the jet propulsion engine for certain definite conditions of operation. Complete performance figures were not available for either type of engine but those for the two-stroke were based on existing experimental data and those for the jet thrust engine on a combination of theory and experiment.

THE CHAIRMAN asked whether there was any criticisms of the calculations, if the data was accepted. MAJOR GREEN thought that the capabilities of the 'Spitfire' had been stretched rather highly in Report 6102.

MR RICARDO referred to the different ratings assumed for the two-stroke in papers 6103 and 6102 and MR MORLEY explained that allowance had been made in the bmep for development in the next few years; the air consumption had also been increased by 24% causing an increase in the ihp of 6%. The same efficiency had been taken for the supercharger and it had been assumed that the intercooler could deal with the extra charge cooling power. The engine speed had been increased to 3000 rpm in view of Mr Ricardo's opinion that the speed of 2750 rpm used in 6102 was low.

THE CHAIRMAN then asked Mr Wood what bmep he expected would be possible with the two-stroke in a year or two's time. MR WOOD replied that results on the Rolls-Royce complete engine had closely checked the Ricardo single-cylinder results at the same boost pressure. MR RICARDO added that a figure of 270 lb/sq.in had been obtained on the single-cylinder unit with 100 octane fuel.

THE CHAIRMAN asked Mr Wood what he thought of the engine conditions assumed in Table 2 of Report 6102 where a speed of 3500 rpm was specified. MR WOOD replied that this speed seemed to him rather high. In view of the 6½" stroke on the Rolls-Royce engine as compared with 5½" on th e Ricardo units he thought 3000 rpm was not likely to be much exceeded. THE CHAIRMAN said it appeared to him that the two-stroke engine had a marked superiority over the Griffon and he had hoped at one time that it would take the place of the Merlin. This was not to be, it seemed, since the two-stroke was not ready. He therefore asked Mr Wood to let the

Sub-Committee have his opinion on the present position of the two-stroke.

MR WOOD said that the problems confronting his Company now were mechanical ones, concerned mainly with sleeve and piston lubrication . In contrast to Messrs Ricardo's use of a high carbon steel as a sleeve material the Rolls-Royce Co were using austenitic steel sleeves which were difficult to wet with oil. The two-stroke piston was a long one overrunning the ports and the net result was that the gas pressure on the top ring, in conjunction with the turning movement of the sleeve, caused excessive ring wear and sometimes breakage. In order to improve the lubrication properties of the sleeve they had tried shot-blasting the surface and had completed a test of 150 hours, but the results had not been so good more recently. This was probably due to the honing which was necessary after the shot-blasting process. Other processes which were being tried were etching, basket grinding and rough grinding. The present position was that, with a shot-blasted and honed sleeve, the ring wear after 50 hours running in the 12-cylinder engine was 2½/1000 inch . THE CHAIRMAN asked the reason for not using the carbon steel sleeves. MR WOOD explained that the austenitic steel was used to meet the cold starting requirement which was that the engine should be capable of being started at -10°C, and the lower coefficient of expansion of the carbon steel sleeve caused too great a reduction of clearance at the low temperature. The alternative of using Lo Ex alloy cylinders had not been possible owing to the difficulty of getting cylinder blocks cast in this material. In answer to the Chairman's question, MR WOOD said that the Birmingham Aluminium Co. were proposing to cast cylinders in a silicon aluminium alloy which had better casting properties than Lo Ex and which was, in fact, similar to that used on German engines.

THE CHAIRMAN thought it would be unwise to use materials for sleeve and cylinder of greatly different thermal expansion, in view of the high performance which would be required from the engine. He asked whether it would be possible to obtain uniform finish on the sleeves and MR WOOD replied that it would be possible to specify the degree of surface finish on the drawing and to check it with a surface analysing machine. MR CONSTANT asked whether the special surface might not be worn out within the life of the engine and MR WOOD said that this question was being studied. THE CHAIRMAN asked whether there were any other troubles in the new engine. MR WOOD said there were no other troubles. The bearings behaved well and were far more easily made than those fitted on the Merlin. THE CHAIRMAN suggested that if all these troubles were likely to be cleared up in a year's time, it would be worth while to start making arrangements for production of the engine immediately. MR WOOD, however, thought that this procedure would be risky and that it would be wiser to complete the development first. He was of the opinion that the greatest help would be gained if the Sub-Committee recommended the consideration of more engines for development purposes.

MR CORBITT said that one of the most important factors was the amount of excess scavenge air which was to be used. He referred to Fig. 8 in Report 5750, ICE1447, [RAE report E.3932] saying that he thought the shape of the curves was misleading. Up to a scavenge air consumption of 1.6 swept volume the total engine power was still increasing, whereas the figure gave the impression that the minimum air consumption for maximum torque was obtained at 1.2 swept volumes. It was now proposed to use 55% of excess air at the boost temperature and pressure on the complete engine. MR MORLEY pointed out that the use of the excess air would adversely affect the cruising performance, causing an increase in specific fuel consumption of 5-10%. Referring to Table 1 in Report 6103, MR CORBITT said that the powers tabulated should be obtainable without the use of an intercooler. He thought the basic bmep was pessimistic and the fuel consumption far higher than they were actually obtaining at present. The present figure was nearer 14 lb/min, corresponding with 0.35 lb/ihp/hr or 0.38 lb/shp/hr. MR MORLEY said that his figure of 23.4 lb/min corresponded with 0.55 lb/hp/hr, but MR WOOD said that all the recent running with the two-stroke engine had been carried out at the lower rate of fuel consumption, under which conditions the engines seemed to be equally reliable.

Turning to the fuel consumption of the jet propulsion unit, THE CHAIRMAN asked Wing Commander Whittle for his opinion on the figures in Table 3 of Report 6103. WING CDR WHITTLE said that the best fuel consumption figure on static thrust now corresponded with 1.04 lb/bhp/hr and if a figure greater than 1.115 lb/bhp/hr was recorded it was considered a bad one. [Jet engine fuel consumption is usually expressed as lb/lb thrust; presumably a conversion to an equivalent lb/bhp figure was used to give a more accurate comparison.] He thought that an improvement of 11-12% should be possible in about a year's time when the effect of thrust augmentors would be felt. MR CONSTANT said that there was little knowledge of the manner in which fuel consumption and jet thrust varied with altitude. He said that the matter was bound up with compressibility effects and that the figures presented probably gave pessimistic ground level performance and an optimistic variation of thrust with altitude. WING CDR WHITTLE said that the figures given in the paper were based on present jet propulsion results and gave a fair estimate of performance. He considered, however, that the basis of comparison with the two-stroke might have been better chosen. He suggested that it would have been fairer to design an aircraft for specified ranges rather than for fixed endurances. He thought, however, that on this basis there would be no alteration in the main conclusions. MR PERRING pointed out that the basis of comparison was quite deliberate and was chosen with particular reference to Fleet Air Arm requirements where long endurance was essential. THE CHAIRMAN said it could now be concluded that for the short endurance intercepter fighter, particularly at great altitudes, jet propulsion was the best. MR MORLEY remarked that there was not much difference in maximum speed at 40,000 ft, but THE CHAIRMAN pointed out that the jet propulsion plant had a big advantage in lightness, being only three-quarters of the weight of the two-stroke engine giving comparable speed. This reduction of weight would give an increase in rate of climb as had evidently been sought for in the German FW190 where some speed had been sacrificed to get higher rate of climb.

WING CDR WHITTLE reminded the Sub-Committee of the effect which the thrust augmentor would have, but as THE CHAIRMAN pointed out the jet unit was better even now for endurance at great altitudes. MR MORLEY said that the change-over in advantage from one type to the other occurred at an endurance of two hours and a height of 20,000 ft. MR CONSTANT added that the jet propulsion unit was best for short range at any altitude or for longer range at high altitude. The two-stroke was most suited to long range and high performance at low altitude.

THE CHAIRMAN said there was little doubt that it would be necessary to accept the need for two types of fighter. He was not sure if it was advisable to continue the development of a two-stroke of the present size, since by the time it was in production the Spitfire would probably have an engine housing suitable for the Griffon. MR WOOD thought there was much to be said for concentrating on a two-stroke engine of the present size, but he visualised the use of such an engine in a special aircraft. In this aircraft only about a quarter of the total power would be converted into thrust by the propellor, the exhaust from the two-stroke engine passing through a turbine driving a fan in a duct connected with the radiator outlet. All the hot gases would then pass to the rear of the machine to form a high-powered jet. WING CDR WHITTLE had been thinking of a similar scheme independently, but in his case the external propellor was to be entirely eliminated. MR CONSTANT reminded the Sub-Committee that Mr Ricardo had been working before the war on a project of the same type in which better fuel economy should be obtained but at the cost of greater weight. The need for and difficulty of obtaining contra-rotating airscrews was mentioned by PROF BAIRSTOW but MR CONSTANT said this difficulty could be got over by the use of a power turbine having two contra-rotating rotors. It was agreed that such a power plant would have the advantage of lower fuel consumption and therefore long range owing to the higher expansion ratio in the turbines and would probably be most suitable for a heavy bomber.

THE CHAIRMAN said he thought that an important stage in aircraft development had been reached and that a definite recommendation from the Engine Sub-Committee was required as to present policy. The Sub-Committee were agreed that the jet propelled aircraft was best for short range interception. High performance at low altitude was better obtained from the two-stroke or the Griffon, particularly where longer range was needed. The choice of policies before the Sub-committee were: (1) to urge for an increase of speed in development of the two-stroke as at present designed; (2) to devote the same energy to a two-stroke engine of the same size as the Griffon; (3) to depart from conventional aircraft plants and initiate the design of a ducted fan system such as the one proposed by Messrs Rolls-Royce. In any case it was now becoming evident that the aircraft should be designed for the power plant as well as the power plant for the aircraft. This was most necessary in order to get satisfactory flow of the exhaust gas into the jet and with this view the Sub-Committee heartily agreed. It was decided, therefore, to make no immediate recommendation, but to give the question further consideration after the Minutes had been studied.

MOST SECRET

ENGINE SUB-COMMITTEE
AERONAUTICAL RESEARCH COMMITTEE

Minutes of the Conference held between the Engine Sub-Committee, (141st) and members of the Technical Staff of Messrs Rolls-Royce at Derby, on 21st July 1943.

Present:- Prof L Bairstow, Mr H Constant, Sir Alfred Egerton, Mr W S Farren, Mr H M Garner, Major F M Green, Capt C M Hall RN, Sir Melvill Jones, Mr B Lockspeiser, Dr D R Pye, Mr H R Ricardo, Major A A Ross, Mr A O Saunders, Mr A F C Brown. Prof. P M S Blackett, Mr W G L Perring, Dr H C H Townend and senior members of the Rolls-Royce technical staff were present.

Two-stroke petrol-injection engine and exhaust utilisation

MR WOOD described the two-stroke petrol-injection engine, mentioning the special sleeve drive and the large capacity centrifugal blower. Utilisation of the exhaust energy could be effected in three ways, (1) with a jet, (2) with a turbine geared to the crankshaft , (3) by means of a thrust augmenter.

Problems which had had to be faced were the production of a magneto to spark at twice the normal rate and an injection pump to run at twice the normal speed. The magneto problem had been surmounted by the use of a condenser discharge and transformer which worked well up to 3000 rpm. No trouble had been experienced with the injection pump, the only necessary precaution being the use of high-pressure oil seals and oil lubrication of the plungers.

Difficulty had been experienced in piston lubrication. The KE.965 steel sleeve had been found difficult to wet but this had been overcome by machining grooves in the sleeve with corresponding grooves in the piston. Piston cooling, however, was still an unsolved problem. The piston required 35-40 gal/hr/piston, and so far it had not been possible to get this quantity of oil up the hollow connecting rods; but the end-to-end system of crankshaft oil supply was being introduced to conserve the amount of oil supplied to the main and eccentric bearings.

DR PYE asked how the engine itself compared in power with the Merlin engine. DR HOOKER replied that the present two-stroke was 78% larger in capacity than the Merlin (allowing for the number of firing strokes being doubled) but that owing to the volumetric efficiency being lower the brake horse-power of the two-stroke for equal boost was only 25% greater without allowing for the greater exhaust power of the two-stroke engine. MR WOOD added that the two-stroke was wider owing to it being a 90°-vee, but otherwise similar to the Merlin. The installed weight complete with jets was about 3000 lb. The heat to be dissipated was the same as for the Merlin but a greater proportion of heat went to the oil and less to the cylinder jackets. The fuel consumption was about 0.44 pints/ihp/hr.

In answer to a question from SIR MELVILL JONES, DR HOOKER compared the power of the two-stroke with that of the Merlin in greater detail. Comparing the brake horse-power of the two engines the two-stroke was now 30% more powerful than the Merlin with a single-stage supercharger and 17% greater with a two-stage supercharger. [This statement was queried in the margin – Ed] When both two-stroke and four-stroke engines were fitted with ejector manifolds of the most efficient type, the over-all power of the two-stroke would be 25-30% greater than that of the Merlin depending on aircraft speed and 5-10% greater than that of the Griffon and this would be increased by using an exhaust-driven turbine geared to the crankshaft.

MR CORBITT amplified this statement by saying that with improved valve timing and ports and using a blower having a 5:1 pressure ratio it was hoped to get as much power from the exhaust (using a turbine and a jet) as from the pistons at 450 mph. This was based on test results made with a WR1 turbine wheel. With the new blower it was necessary to apply exhaust back pressure indicating a greater power available in the exhaust. It seemed certain that a simple jet would be too noisy and it was proposed to pass the exhaust first through a 12″-diameter, WR.1-type turbine disc before a final jet. Possibilities were to gear the turbine directly to the engine or to couple it to a turbo-blower. If the W2B turbine disc was used the power would be in excess of that required for the blower and the turbine would be coupled to the engine. [The WR.1 was Rolls-Royce's first gas turbine to run and was based on the Whittle design. The W2B was Whittle's design taken over by Rolls-Royce and put into service as the Welland.]

* * * * *

Rg/Cbt 1/JC 14.9.44

Comparison of Crecy & Merlin engines

The Crecy BHP estimated in Lov/SGH 6/JS 1.11.42 has now been exceeded by 12% on the Crecy main engine and the Merlin/Crecy comparison should be brought up-to-date.

According to the above comparison the Crecy was 35% better than the Merlin when utilising the exhaust energy; this now becomes 50%.

The following note gives a detailed comparison of Crecy and Merlin performance which shows that the value of the Crecy depends on the utilisation of its exhaust energy.

With the turbine instructed for the Crecy it should be superior to a similarly equipped Merlin by about 50% in power and 15% in consumption at 15,000 ft. The bare engine weights are approximately 1440 lb for Merlin and 1640 lb for Crecy.

The provision of the exhaust cooling necessary with the Merlin will probably lead to equal weights for the two turbine systems.

The present Crecy engine shows considerably less performance than the Merlin when run on the test bed. This is due to the use of lower speeds and boosts and lack of an intercooler at the present stage of development.

A typical comparison is:-

	Merlin	Crecy
RPM	3000	2600
Boost Pressure (lb)	30	15
Intercooled	yes	no
BHP	2340	1600

The Crecy rated altitude is also considerably lower owing to its small blower capacity. This causes the working point efficiency to fall rapidly with increasing speed so that at 2.5 compression ratio the Crecy working point is already 8% below peak efficiency.

Assuming boost, speed and blower efficiency to be the same, there is a difference in performance in favour of the Merlin above 15,000 ft if bare engine powers are considered. The relative performance figures cross over in favour of the Crecy at all altitudes, however, when the exhaust energy is taken into account, either in the form of plain jets or with the use of a turbine.

The magnitude of this gain will be seen from the following table for the conditions of 400 mph, 15,000 ft, 20 lb boost, 3000 rpm, supercharger, intake and airscrew efficiency 80%, turbine efficiency 83% and jet efficiency 90% and no intercooler.

	Merlin	Crecy
BHP with no exhaust utilisation	1661	1625
BHP with jets	1602	1625
Nett jet HP	241	865
Total HP with jets	1843	2490
BHP (allowing for back pressure)	1462	1625
Turbine HP	450	1100
Residual jet HP	95	265
Total HP with turbine installation	2007	2990

In this table BHP means SHP less blower HP and it will be seen that the Merlin BHP drops 200 when back pressure is applied to give optimum performance with turbine.

The Crecy on the other hand already requires back pressure in order to generate maximum BHP and for the 15,000 ft case this particular back pressure is the same as that which gives optimum performance with turbine. There is thus no loss of BHP when the turbine is applied.

2-Stroke Engine Division, Rolls-Royce Limited December 1944

2-Stroke v 4-Stroke

Introduction

After 3½ years of experimental work it is now possible from existing data to draw some comparisons between 2-stroke and 4-stroke engines and to forecast the place the former engine has in any future aircraft programme in relation to the 4-stroke engine and the jet engine.

In comparing 2-stroke and 4-stroke engines, although both have similar parts such as cylinders, pistons, valves, connecting rods, crankshafts, etc., there is no resemblance between the functions these parts perform nor in the methods of controlling the power from the two engines.

In the 4-stroke-cycle engine every alternate revolution is devoted to the function of emptying and refilling the cylinder. In the 2 -stroke-cycle engine a part only of the expansion and compression strokes is set aside for this function. This difference between the two methods of emptying and recharging the cylinder affects profoundly the entire functioning and control of the engine; thus -

(a) In the four-cycle engine the exhaust is removed positively by the piston and the empty cylinder is then recharged with a variable quantity of combustible mixture, the power being controlled by the quantity admitted, i.e. by throttling the inlet. In the two-cycle engine the cylinder cannot be emptied, the residual exhaust is displaced by incoming air, but if the air supply is throttled the result is merely that less exhaust is displaced, and, in the extreme, the cylinder will be left full of exhaust gas. Therefore, the power of the engine cannot efficiently be controlled by throttling but only by the quantity of fuel admitted. In this respect its functioning is more like a compression-ignition engine or a jet engine than to a spark-ignition 4-stroke engine.

(b) In the four-cycle engine the amount of air or combustible mixture at any pressure, admitted per cycle, is metered positively by the piston and cannot exceed the volume defined by the piston displacement. In the two-cycle engine, however, there exists, for a period, a complete short circuit between the inlet and exhaust ports, hence the amount of air which can enter and pass through the cylinder bears no relation whatever to the piston displacement. For any given port area and timing it is controlled only by the pressure drop in passing through the cylinder and is wholly independent of speed. Thus at any given boost pressure the same weight of air will pass into and through the cylinder per unit of time whether the engine speed be 300 or 3000 rpm. In the former case it may represent 10 cylinder volumes per cycle, in the latter one cylinder volume.

(c) In the four-cycle engine the same working parts are employed alternately and for an equal interval of time for both the high and low pressure parts of the cycle. In the two-cycle engine the work of emptying and filling is one by the blower alone and the reciprocating parts are used solely for high- pressure work. Also, in the two-cycle engine the inertia of the reciprocating masses is, at every cycle, to a large extent cushioned and balanced out by the compression and the mean loading on the bearings is very reduced.

Control

Since the 2-stroke engine cannot be throttled, control must be effected by varying the quantity of fuel admitted as is done for CI engines and jet engines. In the CI engine this presents no difficulty since ignition and combustion are independent of mixture strength, nor for the jet engine where combustion is continuous once it has been initiated; but for the spark-ignition engine, using a pre mixed charge, ignition and combustion are possible only over a very limited range of mixture strength.

On the 2-stroke engine this difficulty is overcome by working with a stratified charge obtained by dividing the combustion chamber into two portions, within the smaller of which a mixture of ignitable proportions is retained at all times, while the other and larger portion may in the extreme case contain no fuel at all. The combustion chamber which gives the desired effect consists essentially of a small bulb, in which the sparking plugs and injector are fitted, connected through a slightly restricted throat with the main chamber.

The pintle-type injector used projects as the main charge, a hollow cone of spray through the throat to meet at right-angles the air entering through the inlet ports. The injection period is arranged to tail-off slowly and finish up with an injection of low penetration and wider angle into the bulb alone, the intention being that, however small the main injection, there will always be sufficient fuel injected into the bulb to ensure an ignitable mixture therein. The control of power is affected solely by varying the quantity of fuel admitted in the main charge while the quantity admitted to the bulb remains constant at all loads. Normally then, the fuel-air ratio in the main part of the combustion chamber is less than chemically correct while that in the bulb is richer than that. A t full torque the main charge is about chemically correct while that in the bulb is about 50% over-rich giving a mean mixture strength about 10% rich. No advantage is gained with this system by working with any richer mixture for the addition of extra fuel results in direct loss of fuel through the exhaust ports, irregular running by over-richness in the bulb or overheating in the cylinder by the excess fuel coming into contact with scavenge air and burning in the cylinder during scavenging.

Thus it will be seen that the two-cycle injection engine operates with a relatively weak mixture and can do so over a wide range on the weak side of high thermal efficiency.

Scavenging and breathing

On the 2-stroke engine the removal of exhaust products is done by a scavenging process which may be divided into three phases.

(1) Emptying: During this period the exhaust ports alone are open and the exhaust escapes until the cylinder pressure has dropped to the mean boost pressure.

(2) Blow-through period: Both inlet and exhaust ports are open together leaving a free passage through the cylinder. Air flows in through the inlet ports to the exhaust ports displacing ahead of it the residual exhaust products.

(3) Supercharging: During this period the exhaust ports are closed while the inlet remains open and air continues to flow into the cylinder until the cylinder pressure is built up to the blower pressure when the ports are closed by the rising piston.

For high efficiency it is undesirable to encroach too much on the expansion stroke and consequently the port area must be as large a nd the period of opening as short as possible.

With the open-ended sleeve used on the Crecy the exhaust and air ports are on different levels of the cylinder block and the full 360° periphery can be used for exhausting over the top edge of the sleeve and up to 80% of the sleeve can be used for air inlet. The latter is controlled in part by the sleeve but primarily by the piston and experience has shown that the optimum combined port area is obtained when the sleeve stroke is 30% of the piston stroke. Moreover, for a given cylinder diameter, if the piston and sleeve strokes are increased together the engine will run at the same rpm and efficiency.

For speeds of the order of 3000 rpm the various periods required are:-

(1) Emptying: Requires an exhaust lead of 36° crank.
(2) Blow-through: From 100° upwards depending on the mass air flow required.
(3) Supercharging: Requires an inlet lap of 10° – 15°

Thus for the minimum blow-through area consistent with the maintenance of maximum torque at 3000 rpm, a total of 36+100+14 = 150° of crank must be devoted to the emptying, filling and supercharging of the cylinder. This is equivalent to a loss of about 12% of the total expansion ratio and are the requisite conditions for maximum performance at the engine crankshaft. When, however, use is made of the exhaust it will clearly pay to pass more air through the cylinder; this can be done by widening the blow-through period though at some cost to the effective expansion ratio and therefore to efficiency. Breathing on 4-stroke engines is limited in the case of poppet valves by the necessity for having both inlet and exhaust valves in the head and on sleeve valves by the necessity for having the inlet and exhaust ports at one level in the cylinder block and sleeve.

Supercharging

With suitable port timing the pressure in the 2-stroke cylinder will build up to the boost pressure when the inlet ports close and compression commences. The effect of increasing boost pressure is to increase the supercharge but it will also involve a large increase of air flow through the cylinder. This can be prevented by applying exhaust back pressure.

Back pressure

In the four-cycle engine any exhaust back pressure is objectionable because it exerts a positive resistance during the exhaust stroke and increases the amount of residual exhaust products left in the clearance space.

In the two-cycle engine these objections do not apply because (a) there is no exhaust stroke and (b) the proportion of residual exhaust products depends on the effectiveness of the scavenging which is unaffected by back pressure so long as sufficient pressure diff erence is maintained to give the necessary minimum flow. For a boost pressure of 32″ Hg the power and fuel consumption remain unchanged by up to a back pressure of 12″ Hg.

Detonation

On the 4-stroke engine detonation can be suppressed by over-richening because charge temperature is thereby lowered and all residual exhaust products are positively removed by the piston and thereby prevent the next charge coming into contact with hot residuals. As explained earlier this is not possible on the 2-stroke engine and over-richening has little influence on the suppression of detonation probably because the mixture in the main portion of the combustion chamber is close to chemically correct and that in the bulb is already over-rich.

This stratification of the charge in the Crecy 2-stroke engine has a tremendous influence on the detonation characteristics. Because a rich mixture is always present in the bulb – no matter how weak the bulk of the charge – the onset of detonation is thereby delayed and in consequence very high powers can be carried on very weak mixtures. In addition the scavenging process plays a part in cooling the combustion chamber and this is more effective as weakening-off proceeds because total air flow is maintained although the power is dropping.

The limiting powers for detonation are so high on 100-octane fuel that we have been reluctant to carry out such tests on this fuel but by using 87-octane fuel the following results have been obtained and compared with the 4-stroke engines on the same fuel under similar conditions of running and includes one weak mixture power obtained on the Crecy on 100-octane during calibration work.

The 87-octane comparison is given for the Ricardo E.65 and the Kestrel engines both of same bore and stroke running at 2850 rpm, 100°C boost air temperature. The E.65 compression ratio is 7:1 and the Kestrel is 6:1.

For 100-octane the Merlin and Crecy figures are given for 90°C boost air temperature, the same piston speed of 3000 ft/min. for 6:1 CR on Merlin and 7:1 for Crecy.

Brake Mean Effective Pressure
[at onset of detonation]

	87 Octane		100 Octane	
	Weak	Rich	Weak	Rich
Ricardo E/65	145x2	170x2		
Kestrel	150	210		
Crecy	135x2	155x2	250x2	Not taken
Merlin	Not taken		280	328

* * * * *

To:- Hs. E. Sg. Lr. Wd.2/JC.30.6.45

With regard to the projected closing down of the 2-stroke engine development it seems desirable to put on record a summary of the work done, the operational and mechanical problems met and the progress made in overcoming them, and the present position of the project particularly as regards its performance in relation to conventional 4-stroke engines.

This has been done in the attached notes which give a factual account of the above items. The phenomenally high performance obtained on 100-octane fuel coupled with low specific consumptions constitute a complete justification for starting the project and may give rise to some regrets that our terrific war-time development commitments made it impossible to concentrate more effort on it. But taking things as they are it would be very rash to assume that we are near enough to finishing the project, i.e. realising a production engine, at an output and weight to compete with the latest type of prime mover, the gas turbine, unless some unforeseen difficulties should arise in its airscrew applications.

Wd.5/JC.29.6.45

Crecy engine

This project was started on Hs's instruction in October 1939. with 6 designers and 10 detailing draughtsmen – only 2 of whom were R. R. trained. The designs of a V-twin unit and a 12-cylinder engine were started in January 1940 and manufacture and acceptance tests on both completed by May 1941.

Development with 2 V-twin units and 2 main engines from then to the end of 1943 was delayed by repeated sleeve/piston seizures finally traced to defective sleeve manufacture resulting in soft bores. In January 1944 the direction of development was changed and during the next 12 months 8 attempts at development type-tests were made. The 1st and 8th were run to correct 2-stroke engine schedules and finished their full 112 hours but the others were run to 4-stroke engine schedules and failed to complete the time, the failures including fractured sleeves (2 engines), fractured spring drive shafts (2 engines) and a burnt piston.

In January 1945 the development returned to the 2-stroke project engineers but the failures had reduced the number of development engines to one and the period from then to date has been spent in rebuilding the engines to improved specifications, in extensive piston temperature measurements and in preliminary work with the exhaust-driven turbine.

Since the development running started in May 1941 the contract running time to date is:-

V-twin units,	- 8,600 hours
12-cylinder engines	- 1,060 hours [high powers]

Contract running time on other piston engines over the same period has been 125,000 hours.

Engine	Position.	Scheduled Programme.
No.2	Major failure involving cracked crankcase. Specification for rebuild issued 25/6.	Flight engine.
No.4	Specification issued in March for building with up-to-date parts. Parts well forward.	High-power endurance.
No.6	Built to flight specification. On test bed for proof run June 29th.	Bench and hangar type-test for flight approval.
No.8	Building to up-to-date specification with 2nd turbine. Ready end July.	Type-test at 2400 bhp Take-off and combat rating on 100-octane fuel.
No.10	Just completed series of piston temperature tests. Requires set of pistons.	Performance data and high-power endurance.
No.12	Rebuilding with 1st turbine. Ready by July 3rd.	150 hours endurance from 1000-2000 bhp.

V-twin units

No.3 Cracked crankcase after 69 hours type-test running and total running life of 1612 hours.

No.4 At Ricardo's as a single-cylinder unit.

No.5 Running as a single-cylinder for comparison of integral and detachable head cylinder blocks.

No.6 At R.A.E. for altitude test work.

No.7 Rebuilding with strengthened crankcase.

No.8 Rebuilding after big-end failure.

Engine performance

The following performances have been established on the V-twin units and 12-cylinder engines. The use of an exhaust turbine has been assumed in most cases.

For a given boost pressure the Crecy performance is 50% higher than the 4-stroke engine.

For a fuel of given knock rating the Crecy will cruise at twice the power of a Merlin and take off at 50% higher power.

On 100-octane fuel Crecy pistons have operated up to 14 ihp/sq.inch piston area without encountering detonations. The actual performance was 275x2 imep at 3000 rpm. No 4-stroke engine can approach this power output on 100-octane fuel. The Merlin needs 14 lb more boost, 150 grade fuel and water injection to equal it.

The fuel consumption of the Crecy is lower than the Merlin at cruising powers and is appreciably lower under climbing and take-off c onditions.

The engine air demand moves up parallel with the blower surge point and consequently surging never occurs.

By suitable adjustment of engine compression ratio and engine timing appreciable powers have been attained on the test beds at .38 lb/bhp/hr consumption. In an aircraft using the exhaust energy after the turbine this consumption will be reduced to .35 lb/bhp/hr.

The heat to jackets and oil is slightly lower than the 4-stroke engines when expressed as a percentage of the shaft horse power. With a turbine fitted the percentage on a bhp basis is appreciably lower on the Crecy because in this case the turbine power adds to the bhp without adding to the heat losses.

The engine functions in the same way as a jet engine and would be controlled in the same way, i.e. by running to a given exhaust gas temperature. Power will be set by running to an rpm and an exhaust gas temperature with the air kept at full throttle. [But see also discussion on throttling in Chapters 1 and 2 – Ed.] The maximum permissible exhaust gas temperature of 800°C (before the turbine) is normally obtained at 94% of the maximum possible torque and the point of minimum fuel consumption at approx. 85% at 650°C.

To avoid the complications, drag and weight imposed by intercooling for obtaining high rated altitudes, water injection is proposed for the limited periods of take-off and emergency or combat operation.

For altitude operation above 15,000 feet the power delivered from the turbine begins to exceed the power developed by the engine. This reduces the normal fall off in power with altitude and keeps the specific fuel consumption low.

The steps required to make the engine a complete gas generator of the type proposed in the Ricardo – Napier project are simple and involve only the opening up of the engine timing to pass the necessary amount of air. By raising the compression ratio to 9/1 – which can be done on 100-octane fuel – the fuel consumption will be the same as that claimed in the Ricardo project and for the same engine size the petrol engine output would be appreciably higher because all the air retained in the cylinders can be burnt.

Crecy development troubles

The operation of a 2-stroke engine is entirely different from the 4-stroke engine and is closely similar to the jet engine. As there is no exhaust stroke the exhaust products have to be removed by the scavenge air and consequently any throttling of the air results in less removal of exhaust products until the engine is unable to run. Therefore the engine is a full-throttle engine as regards its air [see editor's note above] and power must be controlled by rpm and mixture strength, i.e. the supply of fuel. Roughly speaking, half the air passing through the engine is retained for developing power and the other half helps the general cooling and reduces the exhaust gas temperature and this latter feature makes the fitting of a turbine possible and profitable. The air that is retained in the cylinder is burnt at the same efficiency as in a 4-stroke engine. Consequently to develop the same indicated power as a 4-stroke engine of the same dimensions the 2-stroke engine consumes twice as much air and to get double the power the engine must consume four times the weight of air. So one of the problems is to make the valving good enough to pass large quantities of air with small pressure loss. This has not been difficult, thanks to the self-sealing sleeve, and we see no limit yet to the airflow we can get.

Mechanical problems

The method of driving the sleeve by an eccentric strap driven by an eccentric on the crankshaft results in a large diameter bearing of narrow width. This has caused trouble which is being successfully met by ensuring ample lubrication and by increasing the width of the bearing and the stiffness of the bearing cap.

The oscillating bearings such as the little-end, blade rod bearing and piston gudgeon pin bushes are apt to be troublesome by the sheer difficulty of getting oil in under non-reversal conditions but all these bearings are now working very well by careful design of oil grooves and oil supply.

Piston cooling in any sleeve-valve engine is difficult but is about twice as difficult in a 2-stroke engine because every rpm has a power stroke.

We have developed pistons which are cooler at the same ihp/sq.in of piston area than any 4-stroke piston but as we must operate at higher outputs this is not good enough and considerable design work has been done on oil-cooled pistons to keep the temperatures down at outputs of the order of 12 ihp/sq.in piston area (equal to 2800 bhp on an engine with turbine). We have got to the stage where we have operated satisfactorily for over 160 hours at 12 ihp/sq.in.

To get this oil cooling requires 50 galls. oil per hour per piston and this must be passed up the connecting rods from the crank pin . This makes the design and manufacture of the rods difficult and weakens the big-end bearing and bearing block. We occasionally crack the bearing blocks and frequently crack the big-end bearing. New designs of rods, blocks and bearings are now being fitted to the engines which strengthen considerably these components. In addition action is in hand to try to oil-cool the pistons by a static jet as on Eagles and Pennines.

Sleeves

Sleeve manufacture was originally very difficult because the nitriding process had to be fitted in with Merlin production crankshaft s at Crewe. Considerable distortion occurred and subsequent bore grinding would leave soft spots. Moreover a too generous allowance for grinding was left in the bore and this was liable also to produce soft spots. The engine trouble due to this was repeated seizures between sleeves and pistons and it was some time before the cause of these troubles was traced to this defect in the bores. Once the trouble was recognised the cure was very quickly introduced and since late 1943 the sleeve manufacture has been very good and no case has occurred of sleeve-piston seizure. Improvements in surface finish such as 'satin' finish have helped considerably in the lubrication of the bore and is now applied to the outside as well.

KE.965 sleeves are going out and NMC sleeves coming in and no failures have as yet occurred with the latter material in some 2500 total sleeve hours.

Crankshafts and bearings

No difficulties experienced.

Reduction gears

No troubles (standard Griffon gears) except when loads have been higher than the gears were originally designed for.

Blowers and drives

Considerable trouble was originally experienced with fractured blower spring-drive shafts. These were due to a complicated torsion build up and have been completely cured by fitting a freewheel to the blower shaft.

The blower requirements for the 2-stroke engine were a special problem in that large capacities were required at high efficiency. Although it has not been possible to do much blower test rig work considerable success has been achieved and we are now operating on the engine at 80% efficiency at 2.2:1 compression ratio.

Conical-machined rotating guide blades developed in these superchargers appear to have solved several problems in the construction of large centrifugal jet units.

Turbine and drives

Not much experience yet but the turbine appears to be up to the designed figures and produces the anticipated increase in BHP with the consequent reduction in specific fuel consumption.

The drive from the turbine rotor to the gear train fractured early in the development running due to torsional vibrations, there being insufficient flexibility between turbine and supercharger rotors to absorb the shock of engagement of the freewheel which had considerable backlash. The freewheels have been centrifugally loaded to reduce the backlash and a spring-loaded freewheel has been designed which will eliminate backlash at all speeds.

This is, incidentally, the first time that a piston engine has been run geared to a turbine.

Cylinder blocks

These originally had the heads cast integral with the blocks but were changed for separate individual heads because of extensive cracking round the combustion chamber.

Actually, the integral heads were kept running for some time while waiting for the separate heads by fitting a bridge piece over the top which transferred the stud loading directly to the cylinder barrel.

The integral head is preferred because it is lighter and gives a lower fuel consumption; it has been redesigned and tests had been scheduled to start on one of the V-twin units on July 10th.

Except for a little wear round the exhaust ports in the first 10 hours running no troubles are experienced with the blocks. The separate heads have given trouble through cracking but improved sections and more foundry experience is getting rid of this.

Injection equipment

In spite of the fact that we are operating at high injection pressures (200 atmos) and at least double the speed at which fuel injection pumps and nozzles normally work we have had surprisingly little trouble with these components.

We have had a lot of trouble with fractured high-pressure piping but have cured this by very careful clipping. [not true, problem wa s never resolved – RFP.]

A long investigation into the effect on engine power and consumption of changes in injection rate, nozzle capacity, nozzle setting pressure and pipe bore size has shown that more reliable operation, slight improvement in power, appreciable improvement in slow runn ing and starting can be obtained by dropping the nozzle setting pressure. It also appears that as the engine valve timing is opened out to get an increase in airflow and power then the rate of injection should also be increased and coupled with an increase in nozzle capacity. Otherwise specific fuel consumption increases.

Ignition equipment

Here again the problem was to produce twice as many sparks per minute than normally required for 4-stroke engines.

Special magnetos were developed by B.T.H. and Rotax and after the usual worries with a new design we have been operating satisfactorily for some time.

Sparking plugs

These again have to deal with twice the number of sparks normally used and trouble has been experienced particularly with cracked insulators and lead formation.

We are now using a Lodge RS.997 with considerable success and are running at 2750 rpm 200x2 bmep for a plug temperature of 520°C.

Induction manifold

This is a large single-piece manifold straddling the V between the cylinder blocks. Being in one piece with the bolting faces at 90° the joint has to be made by wedge action. This is not satisfactory and leakage occurs at high boost pressures. In addition the boost pressure imposes loading on the blocks tending to push them across the crankcase face and bending the dowels.

Twin manifolds will cure both these defects and pattern work is in hand to produce these.

General

Considerable cleaning up of external piping has been proceeding in the last few months to reduce involuntary stops and fire risk.

Features which give rise to trouble in other piston engines which do not arise in the Crecy are:-

Two-speed supercharger gearing
Camshafts, poppet valves and springs
Top joints
Carburetters, load separation and unequal distribution
High crankcase bending moment
Sludge in crankpins
Flame traps
Exhaust joint gaskets and studs
Intercooler
Exhaust flaming
Carbon monoxide in exhaust.

APPENDIX II

Running times

There is no doubt that the Crecy was Rolls-Royce's most unreliable engine. In comparison with the Vulture the latter was trouble-free, which is saying something considering its reputation.

The following account is a record of the running times of each engine between certain periods of time taken from the development reports that still exist. Where an engine failed the reason has been given. Not listed are the dozens of incidents where the engines had to be stopped because of minor failures such as broken magneto drives, injector pipes and a myriad of other breakages and leaks due usually to vibration and overheating. There might be two dozen of these incidents within a period and an example is given of a particularly bad period.

The initial development contract C/Eng/937/SAS/C.28(a) covered 500 hours of running. When this was concluded endurance running was continued against contract C/Eng/3771/C.28(a) for another 800 hours, though testing was terminated just before this total was achieved. All preliminary running on new engines and engines that had been rebuilt following failure or modification was done against various contracts covering engine supply and acceptance. This involved running under 'light' conditions of less than 50 bmep to ensure mechanical integrity and bedding-in before running at 'power' conditions against the main development contracts. Hangar testing, in which the engine drove a propellor, was conducted on a separate contract.

Most of the testing was concerned with general reliability, fuel consumption analysis and the development of pistons, sleeve drive mechanism and other unique mechanical details such as, in the later periods, the exhaust turbine and its drive to the supercharger. Oil system and sparking plugs also featured prominently in the investigations. During the periods of running the engines would undergo a serious of 'builds'. These were to embody new modifications or to rebuild following failure, or just to inspect the condition of internal parts.

With the arrival of peace in 1945 came a lack of interest from the Air Ministry in the development of new piston engines and Hives, realising that fighter aircraft were destined to be powered by gas turbines and future transport designs by the turboprop, decided t o call it a day so far as the Crecy was concerned. It would have taken an enormous effort to develop it to a standard of reliability matching that of the Merlin, if indeed that could ever have been achieved, (the hoped-for 2000 hours between overhauls for the Merlin in civil service was never achieved) and in retrospect one would have to conclude that the whole exercise had been a waste of time and effort as it produced nothing of benefit to any other programme except, ironically, centrifugal gas turbines where Crecy super charger airflow ideas were applied.

There are some reports missing from the Company archives but as a running total of times are given in subsequent reports the followi ng listing is believed to be correct, with the exception of Crecy No.4 whose total life is not known.

V-twin engines

The V-twin engines were vital to the development of the Crecy. Their purpose was the evaluation of all mechanical features before their incorporation into the main engines. In addition, such operational parameters as valve timings, oil flows, etc., were also investigated. It was normal practice to employ single- cylinder engines for this purpose but the unique sleeve-drive mechanism of the Crecy made the twin-cylinder scheme more favourable. The units were simple in construction which was beneficial in getting them back into service following failure. Failures of the main engines could be severe enough to write-off major castings and many parts were robbed from other engines in order to get an engine back onto the beds.

Two views of Rolls-Royce V-twin unit No.6 (previous page and above). The rear view shows, behind the flywheel, the large manifolds imitating the air belt that surrounded the Crecy cylinder block through which scavenge air was blown into the cylinders. In this case entry was below the flanged exhaust pipe protruding from the cylinder block. Above the exhaust are the head coolant inlet and outlet pipes between which is the injector in the centre of the head. This engine, like the later main engines, featured coiled injection feed pipes. The front view shows the injection pumps on the cylinder sides and the coolant pump at bottom left.

No.1 13 March 1939 to 5 June 1939.
Compression-ignition.
Bore 5.10 inches, stroke 6.50 inches.
Ricardo-type self-sealing sleeve, reciprocating motion only, 1.702 inches of travel.
Ricardo-type lipped combustion chambers.
Blade and fork connecting rods.
Piston cooled by oil fed through centre of con-rod.
Compression ratio: total stroke 16.5:1, effective stroke 12.3:1.
Commenced running 13 March 1939.
Sleeve seized after 32 hours running. Rebuilt.
Collapse of blade rod bearing across oil grooves after 65 hours running.
Performance above estimate but mechanical reliability to improve before concentrating on performance tests.

24 June 1939 to 27 July 1939.
Water-cooled hot-plates. (combustion chamber throat)
Sleeve seized after 23.45 hours running.
Running time during period 40.45 hours.

11 August 1939 to 6 September 1939.
Sleeve seizure after 54.15 hours running.

14 November 1939 to 17 December 1939.
Eccentric sleeve drive.
Strap failed twice during period. Sleeve-drive studs failed due to partial sleeve seizure.
Running time during period 83.15 hours.
Total running as compression-ignition unit, 291 hours.
Converted to petrol-injection, spark-ignition.

No.2 Compression-ignition later converted to petrol-injection.
Total running time by 16 August 1943, 861.32 hours.

No.3 Total running time 1612.33 hours.

No.4 To Ricardo.

No.5 Total running time 1528.32 hours.

No.6 To R.A.E. Farnborough for altitude performance testing.

No.7 First ran 15 August 1944.

No.8 First ran 28 September 1944. Total running time 273.55 hours.

Rolls-Royce V-twin unit No.6 on the RAE testbed at Farnborough. The engine is buried among the pipes and cables at left whilst the Merlin single-stage supercharger, driven by the engine, is seen at right, its output passing through a Merlin intercooler. The rig was employed in high-altitude performance research.

Main engines

Crecy 2/A252386

11 April 1941 to ? Mk.I
One-piece cylinder block/head.
Supercharger gear ratio 7.65.
First ran 11 April 1941
No report found covering first period of running but tests known to have been terminated due to piston failure after total running t ime of 69.48 hours.

16 October 1942 to 7 December 1942. Mk.I
3 builds for period.
Tests terminated after 35.56 hours due to piston seizure.
Running time for period 67.12 hours.

Unknown dates
No report found but tests known to total 34.17 hours.

26 February 1943 to 5 July 1943. Mk.II
Separate cylinder heads.
Supercharger gear ratio still 7.65.
3 builds during period.
Successful completion of Air Ministry acceptance test.
Running time during period 38.25 hours.

28 March 1944 to 26 July 1944.
5 builds for period.
End-to-end oil feed crankshaft.
Freewheel supercharger drive.
Equal-length injection pipes.
Two engine failures during period – sleeve seizure and spring-drive (to supercharger).
Running time during period 82.33 hours.

19 August 1944 to 3 November 1944.
1 build for period.
Successful accomplishment of 112-hour development type-test between 9.10.44 and 3.11.44 though fractures during running necessitated replacements of parts including a cylinder head and piston rings. Final inspection revealed cracked big-end bearings, pistons, crankcase reduction gear housing and eccentric bearing.
Running time during period 150.17 hours.

13 March 1945 to 18 April 1945.
2 builds for period.
Attempted 112-hour endurance test curtailed after 27 hours running due to piston failure.
Running time during period 49.51 hours.
No further reports found; probably did not run again. If not then total running time 461.06 hours.

Crecy 4/A252387

? to 11 November 1941. Mk.I
No report found for first period of testing but running time during period was 55.59 hours.

20 July 1942 to 19 August 1942. Mk I
3 builds for period.
Successful completion of 50-hour endurance test.
Second attempt at 50-hour endurance test abandoned due to failure of cylinder block due to head cracking.

Running time during period 80.48 hours.

4 September 1942 to 1 October 1942. Mk.I
2 builds for period.
Successful completion of 25-hour endurance test.
Second attempt at 25-hour endurance test terminated after 4 hours due to sleeve failure.
Running time during period 55.18 hours.

No further reports found, but total known running time up to November 1943 was 293.43 hours.

Crecy 6/A442479

8 July 1943 to 2 February 1944. Mk.II
First engine built as Mk II – first ran 8 July 1943.
8 builds for period.
Engine failed after 58.23 hours due to spring-drive failure.
Engine failed again after further 68.23 hours due to fracture of an eccentric strap bolt 42 hours into an attempted 112-hour endurance test.
Running time during period 126.45 hours.

23 May 1944 to 27 September 1944.
4 builds for period.
Attempted 112-hour endurance test terminated after 39.06 hours due to spring-drive failure.
Test continued after rebuild but engine failed after further 33.55 hours due to sleeve seizure.
Running time during period 93.59 hours.

10 November 1944 to 13 February 1945.
3 builds for period.
Attempted 112-hour endurance test terminated after 50 hours running during period due to main-bearing stud failure.
Rebuilt, but suffered piston failure after 41 hours.
During this period there were 44 fractures/leaks in the first 50 hours running and a further 30 in the following 38 hours.
Running time during period 128.40 hours.

11 June 1945 to 21 August 1945.
1 build for period.
Attempted 112-hour endurance test terminated after 95 hours due to sleeve drive failure.
Hangar test with propellor for 40 hours.
Running time during period 132.12 hours.
No further running. Total time 481.36 hours.

Crecy 8/A442480

8 September 1943 to 25 March 1944. Mk.II
First ran 8 September 1943.
8 builds for period. 112-hour endurance test successfully completed.
Running time during period 207.59 hours.

6 April 1944 to 21 April 1944.
Attempted 112-hour development type-test terminated after 50 hours due to spring-drive failure.
Running time during period 73.41 hours.

7 June 1944 to 15 September 1944.
5 builds for period.
Piston temperature tests. No failures during period.
Running time during period 32.55 hours.

2 October 1944 to 8 December 1945.
2 builds for period.
Attempted 112-hour endurance test terminated after 10 hours due to piston failure.
Engine rebuilt with exhaust turbine fitted.
Running time during period 22.15 hours.
Final Crecy run on 8 December 1945. Total time 336.50 hours.

Crecy 10/A442481

2 August 1944 to 13 February 1945. Mk.II
First ran 2 August 1944.
6 builds for period.
Initial running-in period terminated after 7.20 hours due to partial melting of air manifold, found during inspection.
Following rebuild engine failed after 4.37 hours due to sleeve seizure.
During rest of running to end of period there were two cases of injection pump failure.
Running time during period 53.37 hours.

16 March 1945 to 27 June 1945.
1 build for period.
Piston temperature tests terminated due to piston failure.
Conclusions were that single-piece, oil-cooled pistons were superior to the complex two-piece type.
Running time during period 30.27 hours.

25 July 1945 to 20 September 1945.
Exhaust turbine fitted.
2 known builds for period.
Initial running with supercharger disconnected from engine drive and powered by turbo only. This was unsuccessful as sufficient boost pressure could not be attained.
Supercharger drive restored but spring-drive failed soon after.
Following rebuild 160-hour endurance test attempted but terminated after 60 hours, due to sleeve failure.
Running time during period 82.36 hours.
No further running. Total time 166.40 hours.

Crecy 12/A442482

12 January 1945 to 19 October 1945. Mk.II
First ran 12 January 1945.
Exhaust turbine fitted.
4 builds for period.
Turbine drive failure after little running causing overspeed.
Rebuilt without turbine for 112-hour endurance test but engine failed due to sleeve failure.
Rebuilt with turbine fitted but violent backfire resulted in piston failure. Rebuilt again without turbine for further attempt at 112-hour endurance test, terminated after 31 hours due to sleeve drive failure.
No further running. Total time 67.11 hours.

The above tests on the six engines totalled 1705.28 hours running.

Original running with Crecys 2 and 4 ended on 11 November 1941. There was no more running until 20 July 1942 so that the piston failure problem could be investigated on the V-twin engines.

Contracts

V-twin and main engine running only

B.995772/39/C.2b	Research running on V-twin compression-ignition engine.
C/Engs/2499	600 hours research running on V-twin petrol-injection engines.
C/Engs/3259	600 hours research running on V-twin petrol-injection engines.
C/Engs/4340/C.28a	500 hours research running on V-twin petrol-injection engines.
C/Engs/937/SAS/C.28a	500 hours development on Crecy engines.
C/Engs/3771/C.28a	800 hours development on Crecy engines.
C/Engs/945/C.28a	300 hours running on hangar with propellor fitted.
C/Engs/2986	100 hours flight development installed in Henley aircraft.

INDEX

Aircraft

Companies/Organisations

Engines

Illustrations

Miscellaneous

Motor cars

Personalities

Others